This guide is designed to cover all areas of Graphic Products including desi
and production processes. In covering the core features of all the main
present the key subject matter in a visually attractive, unintimidating way. The boo.
used throughout the two years of study as a course guide as well as an exam revision aid and as such
includes many tips on the presentation of coursework. This guide was a long time in the making - we
hope that you will make the most of it.

CONSULTANT EDITOR: GEORGE ASQUITH

- Assistant Principal Moderator For AQA;

- Design And Technology Consultant For QCA.

- Currently Head Of Design And Technology At Greenhead High School, Keighley.

Many thanks to Mike Lock, Head of Design and Technology at Honley High School, Honley near
Huddersfield, for proof reading the early drafts of this guide.

This book is due for return on or before the last date shown below.

WITHDRAWN

Lonsdale Revision Guides

CONTENTS

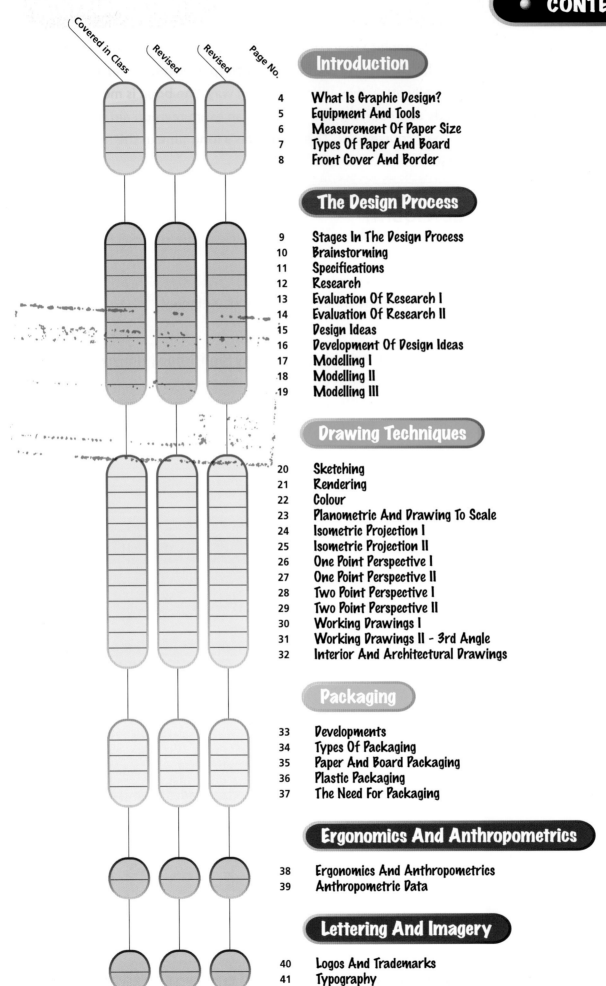

• CONTENTS

Graphic Design

We are surrounded by graphic products; books, magazines, posters and television are everyday examples which we all take for granted.

Graphic design communicates ideas, messages, pure aesthetics or visual statements in the form of pictures and words.

Graphic products can be 2D (two-dimensional) or 3D (three-dimensional). Common materials which are used are: • PAPER • BOARD • PLASTIC

EXAMPLE OF A 2D PRODUCT – BUSINESS CARDS

Their function is to communicate valuable information to clients.

Attractive graphics make the cards more visually appealing and therefore more likely to be read.

EXAMPLE OF A 3D PRODUCT – A PLASTIC MILK CARTON

Its function is to store and preserve milk.

The label contains informative graphics such as the nutrients contained in the product and the sell by date.

Methods Of Communication

1. PICTURES ... are used for visual appeal and to communicate a particular image.

2. TEXT ... gives direct information, but also adds to the 'look' by using different styles and typefaces.

CAPITALS Fine outline

Bold Italic

REVERSED OUT

Shadow

Shown below are the essential equipment and tools which you will be required to use throughout your GCSE coursework and examination.

A3 DRAWING BOARD AND T-SQUARE

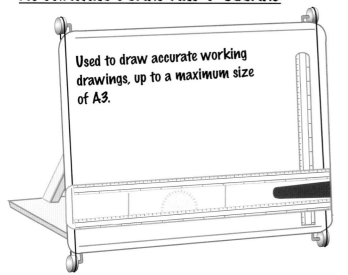

Used to draw accurate working drawings, up to a maximum size of A3.

SET SQUARE

Used in conjunction with a drawing board to draw accurate specific angles, eg. the 60°/30° set square is used for Isometric projection.

300mm RULER

PROTRACTOR

Rulers are used for measuring widths and thicknesses, and act as a guide to drawing perspectives and Isometric projections. The protractor is used to measure angles.

GRAPHITE PENCILS

2B to HB are used for shading/toning. 2H to 6H are used for construction lines.

PAIR OF COMPASSES

Used to draw accurate circles/arcs.

COLOURED PENCILS

Light shading and toning. Some coloured pencils are water soluble and produce a similar finish to watercolour paints.

FINE LINE BLACK TECHNICAL PEN

Useful for sketching/outlining and enhancing lettering. Size 0.5 is most commonly used, but it is useful to have a range: 0.1, 0.3 and 0.7.

FIBRE-TIPPED PENS

Bold shading and outlining. Fibre-tipped pens are either water based, which leaves a 'tide' mark, or spirit based.

Advanced Equipment

If you have a little more money to spend, the following equipment can enhance the quality of your presentation.

ELLIPSE TEMPLATE
CIRCLE TEMPLATE

VARIOUS COMPUTER
SOFTWARE PACKAGES

FRENCH CURVES/
FLEXIBLE CURVES

Paper Sizes

Paper comes in many different sizes. The most commonly used ones are classified in the ...
... 'A' SERIES eg. those given on this page and prefixed by the letter A. They are mostly used for technical drawing and are based on the A0 size which has an area of 1m². The smaller sizes fit within the A0 size ie. 2 x A1 sheets = 1 A0 sheet!! A0 measures 841 x 1189mm and would be represented by the whole of this page using this particular scale.

A1
594mm x 841mm

The thickness of paper can be measured scientifically in units called 'microns'. However the thickness is more often compared using 'grammages'. These indicate the weight in grams of one square metre (g/m², sometimes written as 'gsm') of the particular paper. Photocopy paper and printer paper is usually 80 gsm.

A2
420mm x 594mm

A3 is the best size for most technical drawings and for your coursework.

A3
297mm x 420mm

This is the standard size for a lot of text. This guide is A4.

A4
210mm x 297mm

A5
148mm x 210mm

A6
105mm x 148mm

It's important to choose the right type of paper and board to achieve the best quality finish. Papers come in various weights as well as sizes. For example, a particular paper may be 100 grams per metre squared (g/m^2). This refers to the weight of one square metre. Anything over $200 \ g/m^2$ is classed as board ....

TRACING PAPER
Transparent, hard and strong, its translucency makes it suitable for tracing fine details, drawn with fine lines. Its strength makes it easy to scrape off errors using a scalpel.
Used for working drawings.

CARTRIDGE PAPER/PHOTOCOPY PAPER
Good quality surface for pencils, pens, and markers. The soft surface can also be used with crayons, pastels, inks, watercolours and gouache.
Used for design drawings, sketching, and for good quality marker pen presentations.

CORRUGATED CARD
Two or more layers of card with a fluted inner section to add strength with very little increase in weight.
Used for packing objects which need protection during transportation.

LAYOUT PAPER - 'Detail Paper'
A thin, fairly transparent white paper which provides a cheap medium for designers to use for visualising a project or design.
Used in preparation of final ideas to trace images.

BLEED-PROOF PAPER
Has similar qualities to cartridge paper but specifically good at isolating water-based paints and pens so they don't run into areas where you don't want them.
Used in high quality presentations.

SUGAR PAPER
Coloured paper which has contrasting colours for use in tonal drawings. Different weights and textures are available for different activities.
Used for display work and for mounting drawings, posters etc. but fades in sunlight.

WHITE BOARD
This is a strong medium whose surface has been bleached to provide an excellent surface for printing.
Used for good quality packaging and book covers.

INK-JET CARD
This type of card is treated so that it can be passed through ink-jet printers.
Used to achieve high quality print finishes.

DUPLEX BOARD
This provides a less expensive alternative to white board and also a different texture for printing.
Used mainly in food packaging since recycled material cannot be used for this purpose.

CARDBOARD
This is a cheap, recyclable, stiff board with a good surface to print onto.
Used for packaging, boxes, and cartons.

ISOMETRIC PAPER
A ready-printed sheet with lines already set at 30°/60° and 90° lines.

Used for isometric projections.

GRID PAPER
A ready-printed sheet with lines vertically and horizontally to help draw working drawings (orthographic projections.) The grids are measured in millimetres.

Used for working drawings.

Gaining Extra Marks

To achieve high-level marks for communication, the examiner will look for visual impact and continuity within the project.

Here are THREE pieces of advice that you should follow ...

1. PRODUCE A STUNNING FRONT COVER

This will catch the eye of the examiner. However, you must make sure that the rest of your coursework is up to the same standard. Remember to include important information like: your name, the title of your project, an attractive illustration and a border. A good tip is to produce your cover at the end of your project when your skills have improved.

2. PRODUCE A BORDER

A border can be used to provide a boundary to work within. If you want to include one for your pages produce a <u>simple</u> black border which can be photocopied. Make sure that you draw it 1cm in from the outer edge, to allow for enlargement by the photocopier, and allow an extra centimetre on the left-hand margin so that the work can be bound together without losing any of the content.

3. PRODUCE A CONTENTS PAGE

Number the pages of your project and ensure that they match the contents page, to make things easier for the examiner.

Communication Techniques

You should make sure that you use the following techniques ...

WRITTEN COMMUNICATION

Produce your information in a logical and well-organised manner, using appropriate specialist vocabulary.

OTHER MEDIA

Use graphical techniques, photographs, cutouts, models and mock-ups appropriately, with a high level of skill and accuracy.

ICT

Skilfully use a range of appropriate ICT techniques, in addition to word processing, such as drawing packages, DTP, image editing, and CAD.

How It All Works

This flow chart is to help you understand the design process, as it exists in industry, and to help you apply these principles to your project work.

CLIENT
Find out the background of the client and establish the problem.

TEST AND EVALUATE PRODUCT
Make sure the prototype works. Record results. Carry out Market Research. Suggest possible further developments and give overall summary. Report back to client.

PROBLEM(S)
Carry out research on the problem(s).

MAKE THE PROTOTYPE
Make sure you observe all appropriate Health and Safety Rules.

DESIGN BRIEF
As agreed with your client. List outline specifications.

PLAN OF MANUFACTURE
List each stage of the production in school. Compare to industrial production. Look at quality control and mass and batch production.

RESEARCH
Use questionnaires, assess possible materials and existing product evaluation. Is there a 'gap In the market'? Ensure that your 'solution' doesn't offend any cultural groups.

DEVELOP THE IDEA
Choose one idea and suggest materials and manufacturing processes. Produce mock-ups. Report back to client.

DESIGN IDEAS
Produce a number of different ideas, to solve the problem. Report back to client

EVALUATE AND ANALYSE
Address the pros and cons of your design ideas against your list of specifications.

TIPS
It is important that you work through the design process in order to find a solution to a problem.

The Client

In order to achieve high level grades, you should identify the needs of the client and the needs of a market group. Depending upon the type of problem, it can be extremely useful (although not always essential) to have a realistic client e.g. someone you see frequently or a relative. The advantage of having access to a 'real' client , is that you obtain first-hand (primary) information for your research and it also proves useful when it comes to testing your ideas and final design.

In your coursework you should write a paragraph on the background of your client. Include the following:

A history/background including any social and cultural issues.	Any problems encountered in their daily routine which relate to the design problem.	An assessment of the financial limitations on the project.	Any relevant photographic material (primary research).

This process is used to help decide what product you will eventually make, or what problem you intend to solve. It also helps to identify all the categories which you will be required to research.

As a starting point, a typical brainstorming exercise would look like this ...

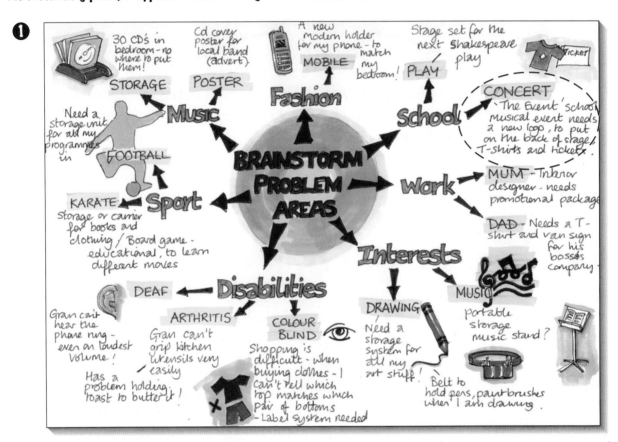

From this, you can now identify a problem in which you are interested, before writing your design brief and prior to deciding who your client is going to be. If for example, the problem identified is the concert ie. 'The Event', then a similar brainstorming exercise can be used to list all the areas of research ...

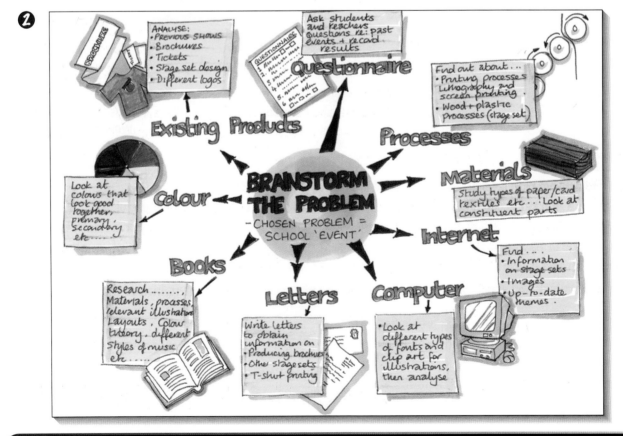

Your specification should provide a detailed description of what the graphic product must have. It should reflect information found in your research and a third party should be able to use your specification to start to plan and develop ideas which would result in a final product. A specification is often best displayed as a bullet point list.

- **TIMESCALE–** What is the deadline for handing your project in?

- **TARGET MARKET–** Who is the person or group of people the design is aimed at?
  - Specify the age or age group and sex of your client(s).
  - What is their occupation?
  - What are their interests?
  - Any details on handicaps, religious beliefs, differing attitudes and values.
  - Are there any socio-economic factors e.g. single mothers?

- **FUNCTION–** What is your design meant to do and what is its purpose?
  Where is this design meant to work? (its environment).

- **SIZE–** Specify exact size or range of sizes.

- **WEIGHT–** Does your product need to be lightweight or heavy for a particular reason? Is there a minimum or maximum weight for your design and will it have to be lifted?

- **DURABILITY–** How long do you expect your product to last? Do you think the materials and cost dictate the shelf-life of your design?

- **AESTHETICS–** In what way should your product be visually appealing?
  Consider the following:- Colour/line/shape/texture/pattern/form/tone.

- **ERGONOMICS–** This is a study of the way in which the human form interacts with its environment. Explain how you could make your product easy to use.
  Consider the following list of information:- Height/width/weight/reach/angle of vision and range of movement.

- **MATERIALS–** What type of materials do you see as being appropriate to make your product from? Does it need to be waterproof/fireproof/easy to clean/lightweight/flexible/strong etc.?

- **SAFETY & HYGIENE–** The British Standards Institution produces guidelines for safety. All standards are given either a BS registration number (British) or an EN European Standard (for more details refer to the BSI website on http://www.bsi.org.uk/education).

- **COST–** What is your budget limit?

- **ENVIRONMENTAL ISSUES** – How easy is it to dispose of, or recycle the materials you use? Does the production of your chosen materials, or the processes you subject them to, harm the environment?

- **MANUFACTURE–** Does your product require a specific process in order to make it?

- **QUANTITY–** Is your product to be mass, batch or one-off produced?

- **PACKAGING–** Does it need to be packaged to be sold to the public?

- **INSTRUCTIONS–** Are these needed to accompany your product so that it can be assembled or used?

- **TESTING–** How could you test your product? eg. trying out on the client is a priority.

In industry, designers spend very little time on research, in comparison to developing ideas. Although, there are lots of areas to cover it is important to realise that research is only a small part of the project work. You should only SUBMIT RELEVANT ANNOTATED RESEARCH. When working out your time, allow more time to design and develop.

There are two types of research:

1. PRIMARY

TIPS
Do not spend too much time surfing the Internet, it uses up too much valuable time and is worth very little marks.

- Interviews
- Visits/Site Surveys
- Analysing Existing Products
- Questionnaires/Surveys

2. SECONDARY

- The Internet
- Books
- Newspapers/Magazines
- PC/CD Roms

COLLECTING INFORMATION VIA QUESTIONNAIRES

Great skill is required to produce good questionnaires. The questions should be unambiguous and not too open-ended. Choose questions carefully, and make sure there is nothing to offend different genders and cultures. Ideally the questions ought to be answered by ticking one of a range of boxes. This enables the results to be analysed much more easily. However, sometimes this is impossible, especially if you are asking a fairly complex question. Questionnaires can be photocopied and handed out, but you may have to push people to get them to hand them back to you!!

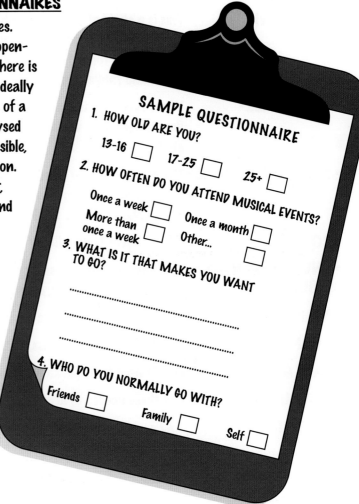

SAMPLE QUESTIONNAIRE
1. HOW OLD ARE YOU?
13-16 ☐   17-25 ☐   25+ ☐
2. HOW OFTEN DO YOU ATTEND MUSICAL EVENTS?
Once a week ☐   Once a month ☐
More than once a week ☐   Other... ☐
3. WHAT IS IT THAT MAKES YOU WANT TO GO?
....
....
....
4. WHO DO YOU NORMALLY GO WITH?
Friends ☐   Family ☐   Self ☐

TIPS
Keep the questionnaire short - think of 10 quality questions.

Keep questions short.

Use tick boxes where possible and only ask relevant questions which obtain useful information.

1. Existing Products

Products which are currently on the market exist for very good reasons. You need to analyse these products to discover why they are successful by asking the following questions ...

- Describe the product, and the way in which graphics are used to promote it.
- What important information is on the packaging?

What?

- Who is the end user of this product. Classify the target group by age or socio-economic group.

Who?

- Why do we choose to use this particular product at certain times?
- Explain the need for the type of packaging.

Why?

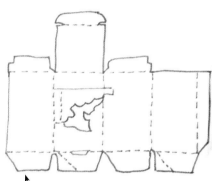

DEVELOPMENT OF BOX
(also called a 'net')

VACUUM FORMED PLASTIC COVER FOR EGG

ALUMINIUM FOIL EGG PROTECTS CHOCOLATE

- Explain how the product works and fits together using diagrams.
- Identify possible manufacturing processes eg. lithography printing.
- Identify the different materials used in production.
- How safe and hygenic is it?
- How much does it cost?

How?

- Where is the product used?
- Where is the product sold?

Where?

- Make sure you label all your diagrams. You can refer to your list of initial specifications to see how you could use this research to help with your design ideas.
- Compare one product against another eg. Cadbury's Easter Eggs with Nestlé's. Identify the pros and cons of each one.

2. Questionnaires/Surveys

If you carry out a questionnaire or survey you will need to collate all the information obtained in order to make any use of it. A table is a good way to show all the possible answers for each question, for example ...

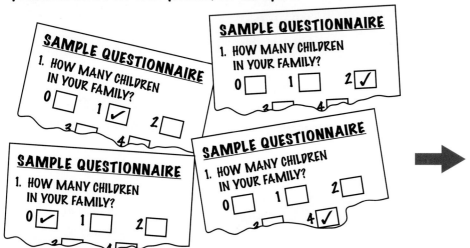

TIPS
Putting information onto a database or spreadsheet can speed up the time taken to collate the information.

NUMBER OF CHILDREN IN FAMILY	NUMBER OF FAMILIES
0	6
1	8
2	11
3	7
4	2

You can then produce line graphs, bar charts, pie charts and pictographs to illustrate your results ...

LINE GRAPHS

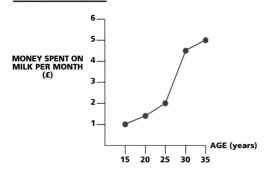

These are useful for showing changes over time. They are a set of dots (or crosses), with adjacent dots joined together by a straight line.

BAR CHARTS (HISTOGRAMS)

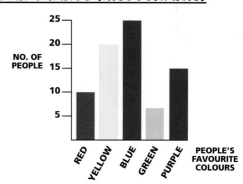

These are useful for making comparisons of results.

TIPS
Make sure you avoid colours and symbols which are offensive to other cultures.

PIE CHARTS

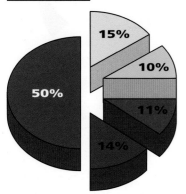

Representing information as a percentage to show clear comparisons.

PICTOGRAPHS

Let 🚗 be 2 cars.

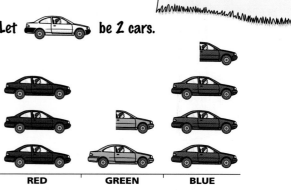

RED   GREEN   BLUE

COLOUR OF CARS PARKED IN A STREET

Diagrams can be used to illustrate your results.

Materials

Design ideas are your initial thoughts on paper, in the form of rough sketches.
Many people may have difficulties in starting off with initial ideas.
Research material which you have collected and books on the same theme,
are a good place to start to trigger off inspiration.

Initial Ideas

Here is an example of a sketch sheet of first ideas.

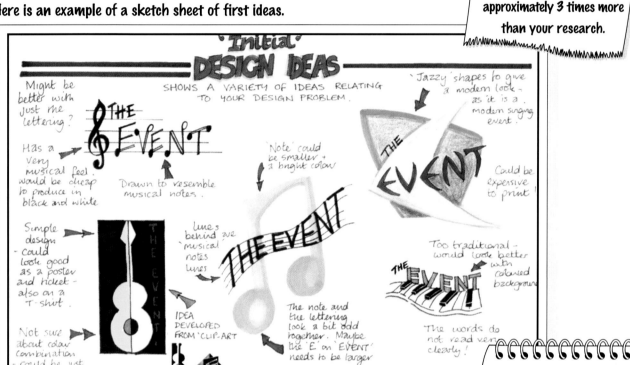

TIPS
Present a range of realistic and imaginative design ideas to achieve marks at a high level. This area of your coursework is also worth approximately 3 times more than your research.

In this example, 'The Event' is a school social evening which needs a logo, tickets,
T-shirts and a stage set. Here the initial ideas have only looked at the logo.
It is a good idea to look at small elements of your final idea before presenting
it at the final stage.

TIPS
You could develop each idea on the same sheet eg. changing shape/colour/style etc. ...
It shows how much thought you have given each idea.

EVALUATION OF INITIAL IDEAS

It is important to analyse everything that you design. Always refer to your specification list to see if any
of your ideas fulfil your aims. There are **4** important questions that you should ask yourself:

Do you think it will sell?

Does it fulfil its function?

Do you think it looks attractive (aesthetically pleasing)?

What is the cost of the product?

Consider the types of materials you intend to use on your design, and whether
these materials are available for you to use in school. You can use computer-aided
design packages to help present these ideas, but at this stage, it is often quicker
to sketch by hand. Also ask and record other people's opinions of your work,
as it is often difficult to criticise your own.

TIPS
Produce a wide range of DIFFERENT ideas - a good range averages around 7 or more ideas.

Whichever design idea you choose, it needs to be developed further. Development means to gradually improve a design in order to produce the best quality product.

MAKE MODELS/MOCK-UPS TO TEST IDEAS

DO MORE RESEARCH AND COMBINE IDEAS

MAKE IMPROVEMENTS TO YOUR IDEAS

... EXPLAIN YOUR EVALUATION

CONTINUOUSLY EVALUATE AGAINST ORIGINAL SPECIFICATION ...

ANNOTATE DIAGRAMS AS FULLY AS POSSIBLE

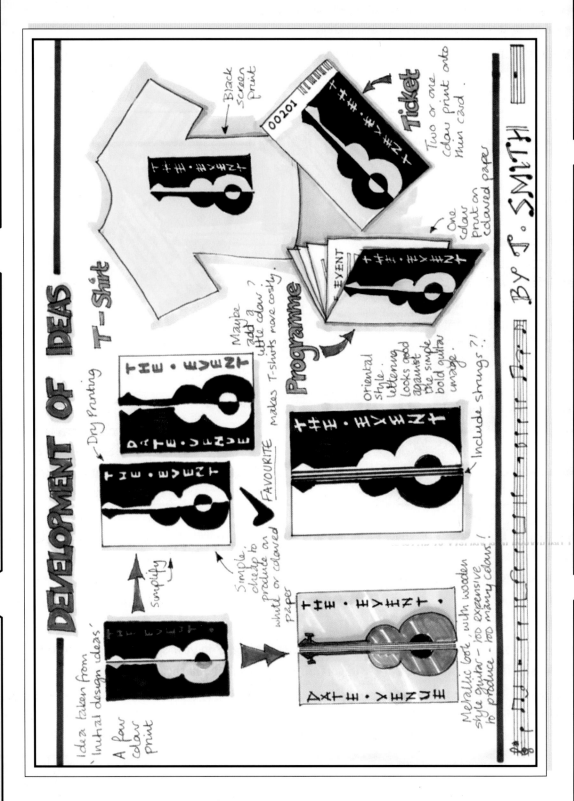

DEVELOPMENT OF IDEAS

By T. SMITH

What Is Modelling?

Modelling is extremely useful in communicating and justifying an idea. Models can be used for the following reasons...
- to make mock-ups for any of your initial or developed ideas.
- to test whether a product works or to do a safety check.
- to show a 3D appearance for the final product.

N.B. Some computer programs can model your design, (even to the point of virtual reality), and enable you to view from different angles. Sometimes, however, this takes longer than sketching a model.

TIPS
- Sketched models should be quick to make. They do not necessarily need to show detail.
- Always use materials and fixings which are easy to work with eg. paper, card, styrofoam, tubes and cardboard boxes (recycled). Use masking and double-sided tape, paper fasteners and staples.

Materials Used In Producing A Model

BLOCKFOAM/STYROFOAM
A dense version of polystyrene, which can be cut and moulded easily, using sandpaper. It can be glued together with the use of PVA glue and will readily accept poster or emulsion paint. Plaster based fillers can be used to coat the blockfoam which can be sanded to shape when dry.

CORRUGATED PLASTIC SHEET
A layered plastic, with two thin plastic sheets on the outside and a fluted centre similar to corrugated cardboard but stronger. Used mainly for better quality packaging, CD and magazine racks and portfolios. Not suitable for MOULDING though.

FOAMBOARD
Thin card on each side, which sandwiches different thicknesses of foam. It is expensive and often used for Architectural and Interior Design models.

HARD WAX
Wax can be melted down and reformed into a mould. It can be difficult to mould dry, as it has a crumbly texture.

PLASTER BANDAGE
Used wet onto wire mesh or other surfaces. It will create sculptural shapes in layers. The plaster hardens when dry, allowing it to be sanded smooth.

BALSA WOOD
A soft hardwood in a variety of different sizes. It can easily be cut safely using a craft knife and a safety rule. Balsa can give smooth finishes.

BOARD
Comes in a variety of thicknesses, sizes and colours. It is the most commonly used material, as it is easy to cut and glue together. It is useful for packaging and Interior Design models.

ACRYLIC (Plastic)
Can be used for modelling, but can be difficult to cut, form and join together, and is also brittle.

MEDIUM DENSITY FIBREBOARD (MDF)
MDF is a manufactured fibreboard, with no grain, therefore making it easier to shape and join together than natural timber (you could use PVA for joining MDF). Its only downfall is that it is an absorbent material, which needs to be sealed first. It accepts many types of painted finishes. Useful thicknesses for graphic products are 3, 6 and 9mm.

HEALTH WARNING
MDF produces a lot of dust when cut and sanded, therefore it is essential to use a mask and to work in a well-ventilated area.

Safety Aspects You Should Follow

Make sure you take the correct precautions and use the following cutting equipment safely and according to instructions given by your teacher.
- scissors • scalpels/craft knives • rotary cutters • compass cutters • scroll saw • die cutters • creasing bars

Adhesives, Fixatives And Masking

The following adhesives, fixatives and masking can be used in various situations.

RUBBER-BASED CEMENT

A rubber-based adhesive. Apply to each surface, wait 10 minutes, then bring surfaces together. Good for photographs and illustrations as it allows for repositioning - not so commonly used now. Has a strong smell.

GLUE STICK

Bonds paper to paper. Produces a fairly weak bond, but commonly used, due to cheapness and handy size. Safe to use and environmentally friendly!

AEROSOL ADHESIVE

Excellent for lighter jobs, useful for sticking complex and delicate pieces of paper. PHOTOMOUNT is an aerosol adhesive specially for sticking photographs to your work. Slightly stronger than spray mount. Safety Precaution- You must wear a mask when spraying and make sure that the room has an extractor fan before you start using it!

POLYVINYL ACETATE PVA

Trade Names: Resin W and Unibond. Excellent for bonding wood or card. It dries colourless and sets in approximately 3 hours but hardens in 24 hours. A safe glue to use, but avoid contact with your eyes. (May be a problem for some people with delicate skin.)

BALSA CEMENT

Balsa wood is good for making models and this is an ideal glue to use on this material. Quick setting. Use in a well-ventilated room and use eye protection.

EPOXY RESIN

Trade Name: Araldite. A two part adhesive mixed together to create a strong bond between most materials, in 4-5 mins. Hardening takes place over 2-3 hours. Safety - A mask, gloves and a well-ventilated room are a must!

ACRYLIC CEMENT

Trade Name: Tensol No. 12. Joins pieces of acrylic. Liquid is applied via a dropper or brush. It 'welds' pieces together. Use in a well-ventilated room - fumes are harmful! Always wear eye protection and gloves.

GLUE GUNS

Glue guns and sticks. The sticks are heated up electrically and pass through the nozzle as softened glue. Glue sets quickly when cooled. Useful in model making or temporary joints. Safety note - The hot glue can burn your skin if it comes into contact.

FIXATIVES

An aerosol spray used to 'fix' soft pencils, pastels or loose particles to paper or card. Cheap alternative is hairspray!! Use in a well-ventilated room and wear a mask!
Other useful fixings include: Single-sided and double-sided adhesive tape, velcro, double-sided sticky pads, staples.

MASKING

Comes in three different forms and is used in airbrushing and pastel techniques.
SHEET - self adhesive, use a scalpel to cut out shapes and stick sheet to paper.
TAPE - Used to mask off small areas.
FLUID - Applied by brush to intricate areas. Allowed to dry, then peeled off.
Safety - Be careful, when using a knife, not to get your fingers in the way and always use with a metal cutting ruler.

Finishes

LAMINATION/ENCAPSULATION

Lamination or encapsulation is when a picture or a photograph is enclosed within two layers of plastic film, which are heat sealed around the edges.

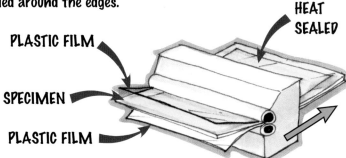

PLASTIC FILM

HEAT SEALED

SPECIMEN

PLASTIC FILM

MOUNTING/PICTURE FRAMING

Cardboard is used to mount pictures using an aerosol adhesive. Alternatively, mounting board (cardboard) can have a window cut out to lay over the top of your design. The picture is attached by using masking tape.

FILLER

PLASTER or BODY FILLERS can be used to fill gaps in your model and these can be sanded down to achieve a smooth finish, especially when using foam.

PAINTS AND INKS

Paints and inks give a protective and decorative finish to surfaces. Paints consist of a pigment suspended in a medium (often a solvent). It is the medium which dries and forms an adhesive film of paint. Most common are cellulose paints (lacquers), oil-based paints and emulsions.

- **LACQUERS/VARNISH**
  Consist of a synthetic resin (acrylic or cellulose), dissolved in an organic solvent which evaporates to give a quick drying paint. Different finishes include gloss, matt, satin, coloured or clear.

- **OIL BASED (GLOSS)**
  Uses a medium of natural drying oil (linseed). It is durable and waterproof.

- **EMULSIONS**
  Contain vinyl or acrylic resin, which are water-based, but not waterproof.

- **INKS**
  Come in 3 types; water-soluble, water-resistant and solvent-based. Most commonly used are water soluble. Mostly used for printing and not necessarily for model-making.

HEALTH WARNING
Always protect your nose and lungs with a <u>SAFETY</u> mask and clean brushes and rags after use, or dispose of them. You should wear gloves or a barrier cream.

Freehand Sketching

This is a quick method of producing an illustration, using a pencil or a pen. It can be used for initial ideas or to explain part of a design. The three stages above show how to draw a pear, without the use of an eraser. The final outline can be darkened by applying more pressure with your pencil.

Crating Out

This method is more time consuming but helps you to sketch objects in three dimensions (3D). If you can't draw straight lines then it would be a good idea to use a ruler when using this technique.

If you want to draw the following object ...

TIPS
Do not use this technique in your exam if you are asked for a freehand sketch.

1 First draw your crate, (a box). Your object will be drawn inside the crate.

CONSTRUCTION LINES

HIDDEN LINES
(looking through the object)

2 Draw one side of the object on one plane of the crate.

WORKING PLANE
(or side panel)

3 Reflect the side panel onto the opposite plane of the crate and draw the same shape.

TIPS
Leave the crate lines on - it shows the examiner how you have worked out your drawing.

4 Complete by drawing lines across from one plane to the other.

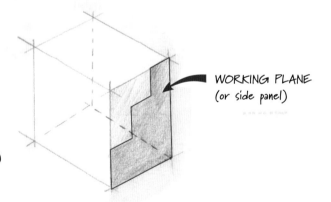

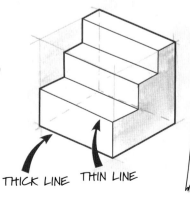

THICK LINE   THIN LINE

TIPS
Any line that connects two faces of the object, one of which can't be seen should be drawn as a thick line. Otherwise it is drawn as a thin line.

Rendering means applying colour and shade to an object to make it look realistic.

Tone

Tone is concerned with light and dark and can improve the illusion of a 3D object. Tone can be particularly effective in black and white, and also where there is a strong contrast between light and dark.

The most important thing to consider when applying tone to a drawing, is which direction the light is coming from.

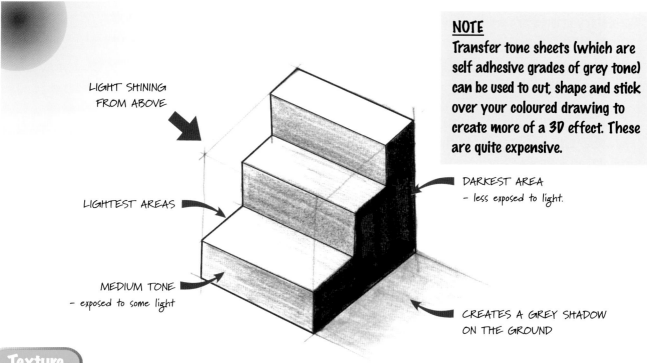

LIGHT SHINING FROM ABOVE

NOTE
Transfer tone sheets (which are self adhesive grades of grey tone) can be used to cut, shape and stick over your coloured drawing to create more of a 3D effect. These are quite expensive.

LIGHTEST AREAS

DARKEST AREA
- less exposed to light.

MEDIUM TONE
- exposed to some light

CREATES A GREY SHADOW ON THE GROUND

Texture

Texture creates the illusion of a surface effect. It is combined with tone to create a drawing that can resemble many different materials. Your choice of paper could also have an effect on the texture.

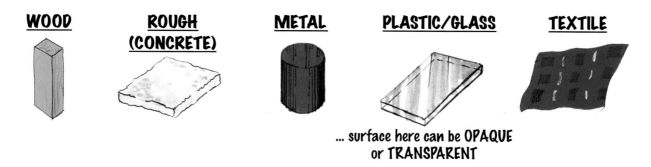

WOOD   **ROUGH (CONCRETE)**   **METAL**   **PLASTIC/GLASS**   **TEXTILE**

... surface here can be OPAQUE or TRANSPARENT

To achieve the above effects and to develop your own technique, try a combination of the following ...

- **MARKER PENS** - These are quick and effective to use. (Look at the illustrations throughout this book!)

- **PASTELS** - Are effective at creating tone - you must remember to 'fix' using a fixative as they can get messy. It may be necessary to fill the grain of the paper with talc before you start.

- **COLOURED PENCILS** - Inexpensive but can be time consuming. Can be used in conjunction with marker pens.

- **AIRBRUSHING** - Time consuming, very skilled and effective way of presenting final ideas.

- **PAINTS** - Again, time consuming and can be messy - watercolours are good as colourwash background.

Primary, Secondary And Complementary Colours

This system applies when using simple paints or coloured pencils.
The following three colours are primary colours.

These colours cannot
be created by mixing
colours together.

RED   YELLOW   BLUE

> **TIPS**
> It is important
> that you understand
> the colour theory - when
> analysing your own
> and existing designs.

Secondary colours are produced when two primary colours are mixed together.

YELLOW ✛ BLUE ≡ GREEN   BLUE ✛ RED ≡ PURPLE   RED ✛ YELLOW ≡ ORANGE

The colour wheel consists of all the above six colours, with the secondary colours in between the primary ones.

Complementary colours are colours which work well together.
These are usually opposite each other on the colour wheel, eg.

BLUE ✛ ORANGE   YELLOW ✛ PURPLE   RED ✛ GREEN

Hue And Tone

Hue is the actual colour you see eg. red, yellow, purple etc.

RED HUE   YELLOW HUE   PURPLE HUE

DARKER TONE   LIGHTER TONE   DARKER TONE   LIGHTER TONE   DARKER TONE   LIGHTER TONE

White is added to lighten the TONE, and black is added to darken it.

Colour Fusion And Separation

Colour fusion is when one colour blends into another eg. red into orange.

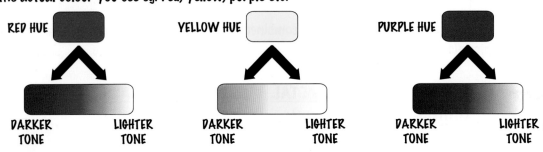

RED   ORANGE

Colour separation is when the design involves printing more than one colour and the artwork is produced in separate overlays.

The Language Of Colour

Colour communicates the mood of the design ...
- BLUES and YELLOWS can look energetic and exciting.
- BROWNS, GREENS and NATURAL COLOURS can create calmness and relate to the environment.
- RED is a hot colour and can symbolise danger.

Paler colours show a mood of gentle, calm emotion eg. PINK.

Planometric

This technique is used to give a three dimensional impression of a plan, by simply projecting the plan into a 3D drawing. It is used to help visualise interiors and for this reason it is usual to leave out most or all of the two walls nearest to you. After drawing the plan view to scale, it is tilted through either **45ß** or **60ß**.

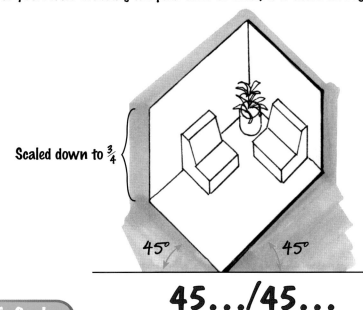

Scaled down to ¾

45°   45°

45.../45...

However, remember that in a **45ß** planometric, the vertical scale is reduced to ¾ in order to reduce the impression of tall narrow rooms.

Drawing To Scale

Full size drawings for Orthographic, Isometric and Planometric Projections are not always possible. Sometimes you need to draw an object larger or smaller than real-life.

• Designers and Architects use a scale-ruler (see below) to help them draw to scale. (The scales are already set out on the ruler.)

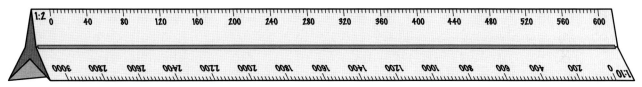

• Scale is written in a mathematical way, called a RATIO. For example if an object is drawn HALF the size then it would be known as 1:2. If it is TWICE the size then it is 2:1.

2:1   **1:2**

Other methods of reducing or enlarging include:-
• **Overhead Projector** - enlarges only. Photocopy onto transparent film then project onto the surface you need to draw onto.
• **Photocopier** - reduces and enlarges up to A3 size.
• **Computer Software** - reduces and enlarges up to A3 size.

Isometric projection is a drawing technique which looks fairly realistic and is commonly used to represent 3D objects. Its main advantage is that you can draw a 3D object to scale.
The following stages show how you can draw a simple cube in Isometric:

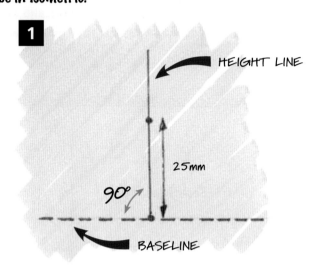

Draw baseline and height line at 90ß - measure 25mm on height line.

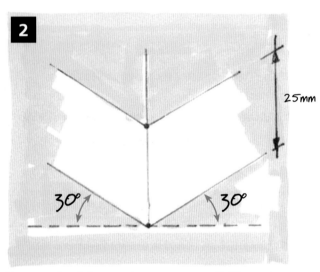

From each of these points draw parallel lines out at 30ß to the baseline

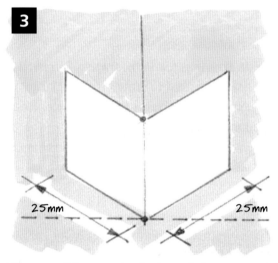

Measure 25mm on both sides of the base and draw two vertical lines - until they hit the top lines.

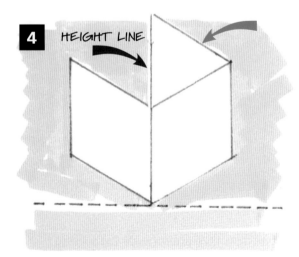

From the top right hand corner draw a line back to the height line which is parallel to the front left hand side.

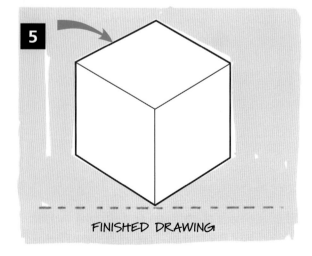

FINISHED DRAWING

Draw in the last line in the same way and then rub out the construction lines you have used to help you.

Drawing Circles In Isometric

Circles in isometric appear as ellipses, and by far the easiest way of drawing them is to use an ellipse template. However it isn't too difficult to produce them freehand by following the instructions below ...

①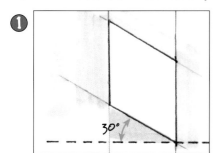

Draw a square plane in Isometric.

②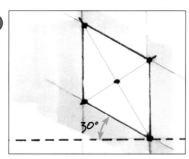

Draw two lines from corner to corner of the plane.

③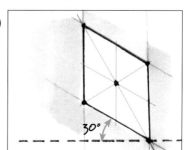

Draw two lines, one vertically through the centre of the plane and the other at 30° to the baseline through the centre of the plane.

④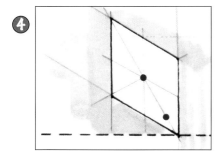

On the diagonal line plot a point ⅔ from the centre of the plane.

⑤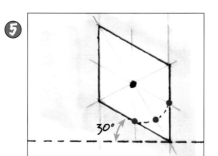

Draw an arc freehand through the 3 red points above.

⑥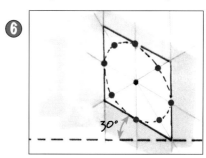

Repeat all around the grid until you have drawn the whole ellipse.

Exploded Drawings

Exploded drawings are used to show how an object fits together. Designers and Architects use this method, as it is quicker than drawing in perspective and helps them visualise what the object looks like, and how it functions.

Below is a picture of a pencil sharpener, drawn as an exploded Isometric.
The construction lines are left in to show how it has been drawn.

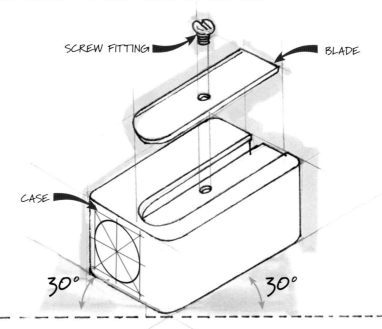

SCREW FITTING BLADE CASE 30° 30° BASELINE

Perspective is how we actually see an object. The furthest point of an object is foreshortened, ie. the further away it is, the smaller it seems to be.

Horizon Line (Eye Level)

The horizon line splits the sky from the ground and is always positioned at eye level.

HORIZON LINE/ EYE LEVEL

VANISHING POINT

Vanishing Point

The vanishing point(s) is positioned on the horizon line. All lines apart from the vertical and horizontal ones meet at this point(s).

One Point Perspective

A perspective with one vanishing point can be used for:
• Quick perspective sketching.
Below is an example of how a pencil sharpener is drawn using only one vanishing point.

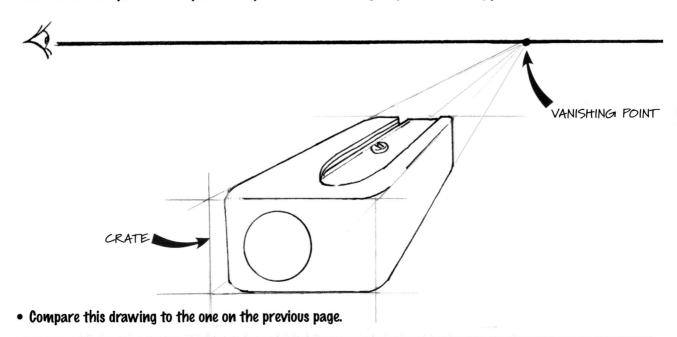

VANISHING POINT

CRATE

• Compare this drawing to the one on the previous page.

One Point Perspective For Interiors

When you draw an interior, the best place to start is by drawing the back wall to scale. It gives an accurate place to start. Standard height measurements can be used.

1

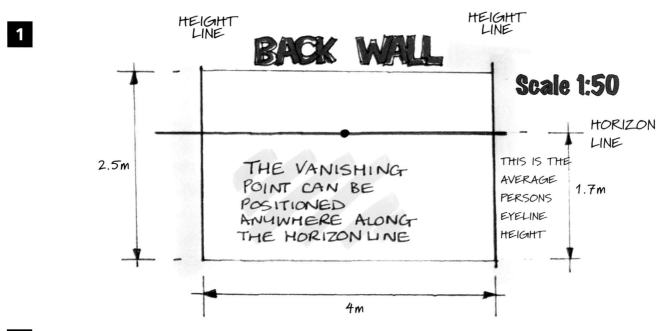

HEIGHT LINE   HEIGHT LINE

BACK WALL

Scale 1:50

HORIZON LINE

2.5m

THE VANISHING POINT CAN BE POSITIONED ANYWHERE ALONG THE HORIZON LINE

THIS IS THE AVERAGE PERSONS EYELINE HEIGHT

1.7m

4m

2 Look at how the cupboard has been drawn in proportion. The measurements from the side and bottom lines of the back wall, have been projected forward. A grid on the walls and floor helps you to establish a depth.

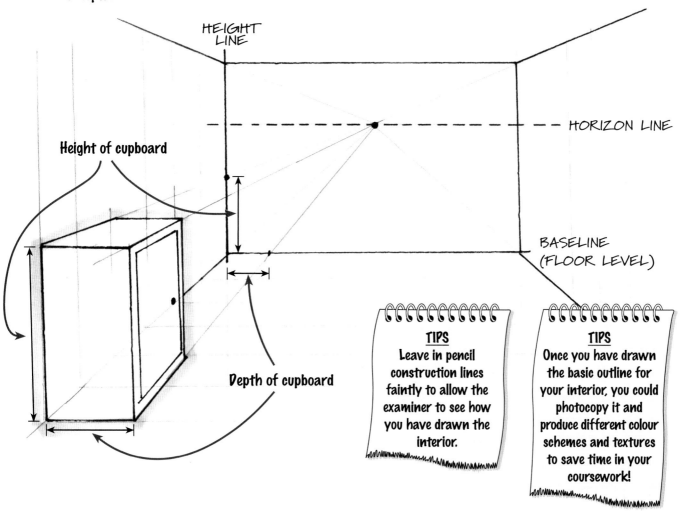

HEIGHT LINE

HORIZON LINE

Height of cupboard

BASELINE (FLOOR LEVEL)

Depth of cupboard

TIPS
Leave in pencil construction lines faintly to allow the examiner to see how you have drawn the interior.

TIPS
Once you have drawn the basic outline for your interior, you could photocopy it and produce different colour schemes and textures to save time in your coursework!

Two Point Perspective

One point perspective tends to give a rather flat image - two point perspective gives a more realistic viewpoint. This time there are two vanishing points, labelled 'left' and 'right.'

Viewpoint In Two Point Perspective

The way we look at an object depends on where it is in conjunction with the Horizon line (eye level). The diagram below shows the different viewpoints for a box.

The words BELOW, AT and ABOVE describe the view you see.

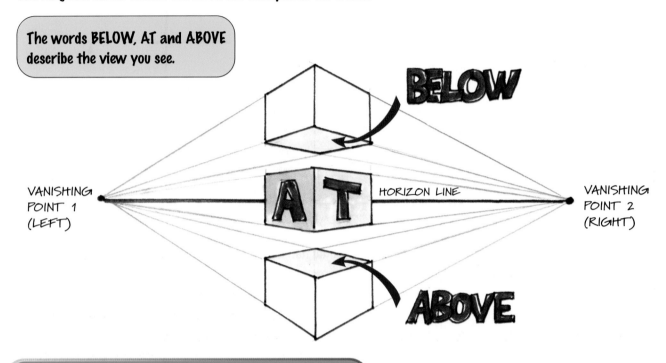

VANISHING POINT 1 (LEFT)

HORIZON LINE

VANISHING POINT 2 (RIGHT)

Drawing An Ellipse In Two Point Perspective

The technique of drawing ellipses is exactly the same as drawing circles in Isometric Construction.

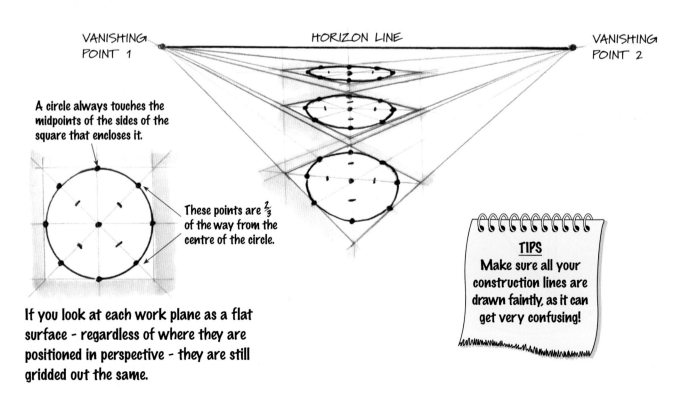

VANISHING POINT 1

HORIZON LINE

VANISHING POINT 2

A circle always touches the midpoints of the sides of the square that encloses it.

These points are $\frac{2}{3}$ of the way from the centre of the circle.

TIPS
Make sure all your construction lines are drawn faintly, as it can get very confusing!

If you look at each work plane as a flat surface - regardless of where they are positioned in perspective - they are still gridded out the same.

Drawing An Object In Two Point Perspective

This is a stage by stage guide on how to draw a simple object using two vanishing points.

FINISHED DRAWING

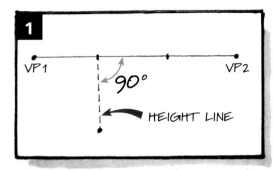

- Draw the horizon line with two vanishing points.
- Split the line into 3. This produces a more dramatic angle. Take one line down at 90° and mark a point (indicating the front, bottom corner).

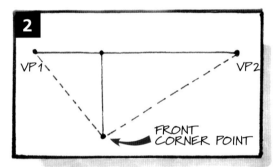

- From front corner point draw two lines back to vanishing points 1 and 2 (VP1 + VP2).

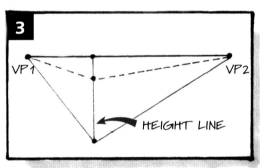

- Mark a point on the height line indicating the height of your object.
- Draw two lines back to the vanishing points.

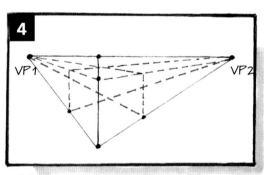

- Mark on the width and depth and draw in the remaining vertical lines.
- From these draw lines back to the opposite VPs to complete the 'crate'.

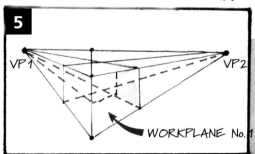

- Draw the side view onto one of the workplanes, and draw in the construction line to VP1.

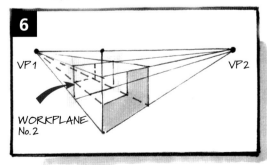

- Complete the side view on the opposite workplane using these latest lines as a guide.

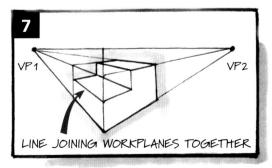

- Join both workplanes together to show the object in 2 point perspective.

The designer will give a detailed drawing to a manufacturer or model-maker to make. The drawings give the necessary instructions for a prototype to be built. Each drawing produced should include the following:-

1. ACCURATE DIMENSIONS

2. ASSEMBLY INSTRUCTIONS

3. SPECIFICATION LIST OF MATERIALS, COLOURS AND FINISHES

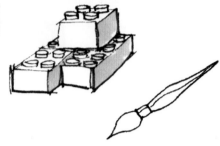

Standards In Working Drawings

The BRITISH STANDARDS INSTITUTION (BSI) has set standards in working drawings that are recognised throughout industry.

Here are some examples of the basic standards required for your GCSE coursework:-

1. Lines

• ───────────────	**CONTINUOUS THICK LINE**	For outlines or edges (could use H or 2H for these) where only one of the faces forming an edge can be seen
• ───────────────	**CONTINUOUS THIN LINE**	For projection or dimension lines (could use a 4H pencil for this.)
• ─ ─ ─ ─ ─ ─ ─	**CHAIN THIN LINE**	For centre lines or lines of symmetry.

2. Dimensioning

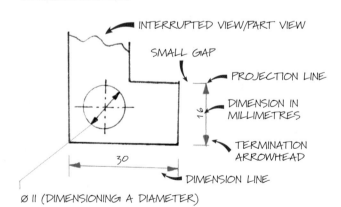

INTERRUPTED VIEW/PART VIEW

SMALL GAP

PROJECTION LINE

DIMENSION IN MILLIMETRES

TERMINATION ARROWHEAD

DIMENSION LINE

30

Ø II (DIMENSIONING A DIAMETER)

- Always use millimetres to dimension your drawing and write the number only ...
  ... this is the recognised measurement for industrial drawings.

- Numbers are always written above and in the middle of the dimension line ...
  ... with all vertical dimensions written to the left of the dimension line. (These are always read from the right hand side of the drawing.)

3. Third-Angle Orthographic Projection

This is the most common way of showing a working drawing. It is an accurate scale drawing of a product.

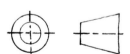

4. Scale

All working drawings are drawn to scale. The scale chosen must be included on the drawing.

Third Angle Orthographic Projection

This is the most widely used form of working drawing. Its purpose is to provide plan, front and side views of the object in question

THIRD-ANGLE VIEWS

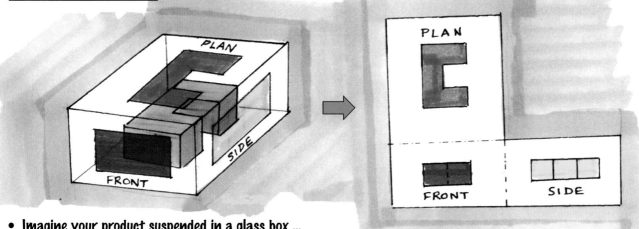

- Imagine your product suspended in a glass box ...
  ... if you draw each view on each side of the box ...
  ... then open it up as shown above, this becomes your THIRD-ANGLE ORTHOGRAPHIC PROJECTION.

- Here is a stage-by-stage set of instructions on how to draw a THIRD-ANGLE ORTHOGRAPHIC PROJECTION.

1

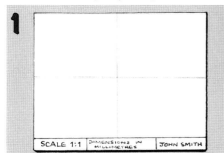

SCALE 1:1 | DIMENSIONS IN MILLIMETRES | JOHN SMITH

- Make sure you measure your page first - so all of the views fit on.
- Then allow a box along the bottom to put scale, dimensions and your name in.
- Divide your page into 4 using a 2H pencil.

2

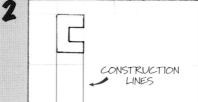

CONSTRUCTION LINES

SCALE 1:1 | DIMENSIONS IN MILLIMETRES | JOHN SMITH

- Draw the plan view first and leave in the construction lines, to help draw the next view.

3

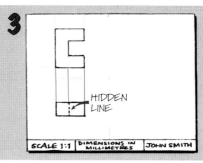

HIDDEN LINE

SCALE 1:1 | DIMENSIONS IN MILLIMETRES | JOHN SMITH

- Draw the front view with the hidden detail drawn as a dotted line.

4

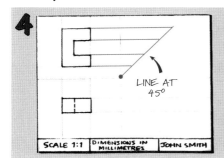

LINE AT 45°

SCALE 1:1 | DIMENSIONS IN MILLIMETRES | JOHN SMITH

- Draw Construction lines into the top right box.
- Also draw a 45° line from the centre of the page.
- Stop the construction lines where they hit the 45° line.

5

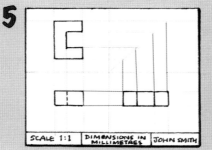

SCALE 1:1 | DIMENSIONS IN MILLIMETRES | JOHN SMITH

- Draw lines down from these construction lines to join the horizontal construction lines from the front view, so forming the side view.

6

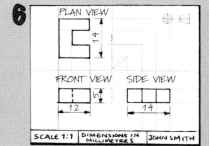

PLAN VIEW
FRONT VIEW   SIDE VIEW

SCALE 1:1 | DIMENSIONS IN MILLIMETRES | JOHN SMITH

FINAL DRAWING

- LABEL VIEWS
- INCLUDE MAJOR DIMENSIONS

ORTHOGRAPHIC PROJECTIONS are used by Architects, Engineers, Interior and Exhibition Designers. For Architects and Interior Designers there are symbols which are commonly used in the industry, like doors and windows.

Symbols

Here are some conventional ways of drawing features.

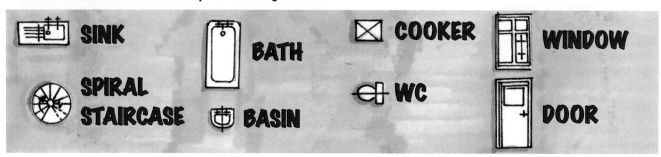

SINK
BATH
COOKER
WINDOW
SPIRAL STAIRCASE
BASIN
WC
DOOR

Plan/Layout Of An Interior

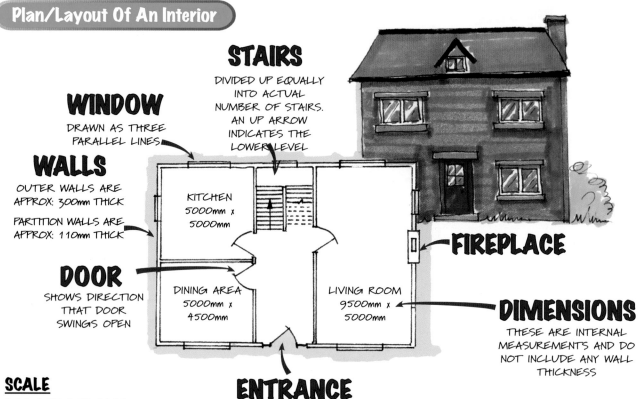

STAIRS DIVIDED UP EQUALLY INTO ACTUAL NUMBER OF STAIRS. AN UP ARROW INDICATES THE LOWER LEVEL

WINDOW DRAWN AS THREE PARALLEL LINES

WALLS OUTER WALLS ARE APPROX: 300mm THICK. PARTITION WALLS ARE APPROX: 110mm THICK

DOOR SHOWS DIRECTION THAT DOOR SWINGS OPEN

KITCHEN 5000mm x 5000mm

DINING AREA 5000mm x 4500mm

LIVING ROOM 9500mm x 5000mm

FIREPLACE

DIMENSIONS THESE ARE INTERNAL MEASUREMENTS AND DO NOT INCLUDE ANY WALL THICKNESS

ENTRANCE

SCALE
1:20, 1:25, 1:50, 1:100
are commonly used in Architectural and Interior drawings.

Exhibition Design

Here is an example of an Exhibition design stand, it is presented in three different ways.

ISOMETRIC
PERSPECTIVE
PLAN

Note: the plan would have measurements on normally.

What Is A Development (Net)?

A development or net is a two dimensional shape which when scored, folded and glued together forms a three-dimensional package, carton or container.

- It is important that all the adjacent edges are equal, so that when they are folded together they are the same length.
- Make sure that the print is the right way up when assembled!

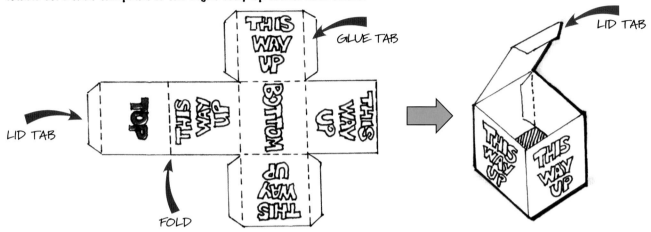

Some Other Developments

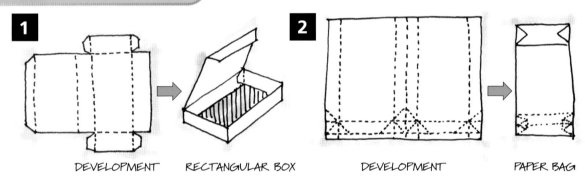

DEVELOPMENT   RECTANGULAR BOX   DEVELOPMENT   PAPER BAG

In industry, developments are arranged on a sheet with minimal gaps between them (called a tessellation pattern) in order to minimise waste. Die cutters are used to press out the shape of the development while creasing bars are used to create the folds in the development. Here is a simple tessellation pattern for a series of developments.

Tuck In And Automatic (Crash) Bases

A 'TUCK IN' ...

... is the tab on the end of the lid, which holds the lid closed. When made commercially it often has rounded corners to smooth out the closing and also has short slits to help 'lock' the lid in place.

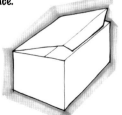

AUTOMATIC BASES
(ALSO KNOWN AS CRASH LOCK)

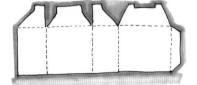

This is a net of a box, which has an automatic base. The box is assembled flat packed, so when it needs to be used, you open up the box by pushing out the base.

FLAT PACKED

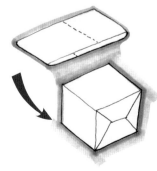

Packaging is a big business and one that we often take for granted. It has four main objectives ...

1 To Preserve

Food products are packed to prevent them from going rotten. Also to ensure that they are sold hygienically and conveniently.

2 To Protect

So that the contents of the goods can arrive at the shops and home without damage.

3 To Inform/Promote

Labels provide information about a product. The contents, weight and how it can be used. They are also used as a sales and marketing tool.

4 To Transport

Goods are packaged into crates or cartons, often called 'outers', so that they can be handled, stacked and transported quickly and efficiently, without fear of breakage.

Origin

Made from wood pulp and waste paper. Board is made to a much thicker and heavier specification than paper.

Paper

Used mainly for paper bags and labels.

Board

Corrugated board is formed from layers of paper which can be formed into boxes for packing electrical goods, books, food packs etc ...
The 'wavy' layer in corrugated card is called 'fluting' which is designed to absorb any impact during transportation.

Lamination

Paper and Board can be used in conjunction with layers of foil and plastic together, to form a lamination.

ADVANTAGES OF PAPER AND BOARD PACKAGING ARE:-

1. Materials are lightweight.

2. Easy to handle and store.

3. Easy to fold and crease.

4. When laminated with foil or plastic a seal can be created to prevent evaporation and also to preserve the product.

5. Colour printing can be produced to a high quality.

6. Environmentally friendly, since they can be recycled.

PVC

POLYVINYL CHLORIDE:
Bottles for shampoo, juice. Blister packs for DIY etc...

HDPE

HIGH-DENSITY POLYTHENE:
Detergent bottles, milk, fruit juice and bottle caps.

LDPE

LOW-DENSITY POLYTHENE:
Bin liners, squeezy bottles, bags.

PLASTIC PACKAGING

PS

POLYSTYRENE:
Egg cartons, yoghurt pots, food trays and bottle caps.

PP

POLYPROPYLENE:
Squeezy bottles for sauce, bottle caps. Film packs for biscuits and crisps.

PET

POLYESTER (POLYETHYLENE TEREPHTHALATE):
Fizzy drink bottles. Oven ready meal roasting bags.

Which Packaging To Use?

Different types of product need to be protected differently.

- Some products are affected by light and oxygen
  eg. Oils, coffee and fat.

- Some foods are affected by moisture
  eg. Meat and biscuits.

- Some drinks can absorb smells and taste
  eg. Mineral water and milk.

PET

A stiff, tough plastic needed for fizzy drinks - keeps the fizz in and the smells out!

PP

A resistant plastic used for sauce bottles and paint pots. This plastic is robust during stacking and storage. Can also withstand high temperatures eg. 120°C.

LDPE, HDPE AND PET
Are also used for frozen foods, and can withstand extreme cold.

PP, PS AND PVC
Commonly used for foods which are chilled and not frozen. eg. desserts and fresh salad or vegetables.

Pros And Cons Of Various Types Of Packaging

MATERIAL	ADVANTAGE	DISADVANTAGE	USE
Paper & Card	Low Density Low Cost	Affected by Water/Moisture	Toys, Cereals, Washing Powders
Plastic (Thermoplastic)	Low Density, Waterproof Can Be Reheated	Affected by Heat	Drinks, Shampoos etc ...
Metal e.g steel, aluminium	Strong Waterproof	Expensive High Density	Tinned Food, Fizzy Drinks
Glass	Waterproof Transparent	Shatters, Expensive High Density	More expensive drinks, Coffee

Explaining Ergonomics

Ergonomics is the application of scientific information (concerning humans) to the design of objects, systems and the environment, for human use. Designers always look at ergonomics with a view to making things easier for people to use.

Factors To Consider

The following is a list of categories for consideration when designing a new product.

Graphics

If we look at this logo, the lettering is very decorative, but difficult to read from an ergonomic point of view.
It is important that lettering is quick and easy to read on posters, adverts etc ... in order to sell the product.

STYLE AND COLOUR

- It is important to choose a type that is easy to read - particularly for warning signs like Fire Exits.

- Colour contrast is also an important ergonomic factor. The fact that a significant minority of the population are red/green colour blind should also be taken into account.

Anthropometrics

Anthropometrics are concerned with the application of ergonomics to the human form and are used to describe the 'user' or 'target' population for a product.

Definition:-   'ANTHROPO' means 'human' and
                'METRICS' means 'measurements'

Anthropometric data is often produced in a table format.
It mainly represents average measurements of the human form.
See the next page for an example of this.

Here is an example of data for the sitting and standing positions. This could be used for reference in your coursework. More detailed data may be found in your local library.

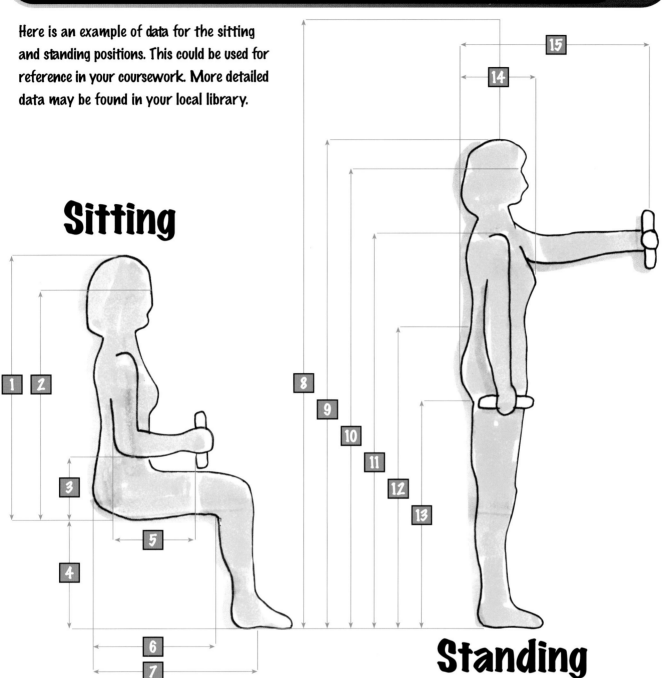

Sitting

Standing

Most graphical products are hand held and special attention should therefore be paid to hand dimensions and the readability of text at varying distances from the eye.

	SITTING	SHORT	AVERAGE	TALL
1	Sitting height	795	880	965
2	Sitting eye height	685	765	845
3	Sitting elbow height	185	240	295
4	Popliteal height	355	420	490
5	Elbow-grip length	304	343	387
6	Buttock-popliteal length	435	488	550
7	Buttock-knee length	520	583	645
	BODY WEIGHT	44.1kg	68.5kg	93.7kg

	STANDING	SHORT	AVERAGE	TALL
8	Vertical grip reach	1790	1983	2190
9	Stature	1505	1675	1855
10	Eye height	1405	1568	1745
11	Shoulder height	1215	1368	1535
12	Elbow height	930	1048	1180
13	Knuckle height	660	738	825
14	Chest depth	210	250	285
15	Forward grip reach	650	743	835

These tables give a range of data from smallest to largest sizes. <u>ALL MEASUREMENTS ARE IN MILLIMETRES.</u>

- Logos are symbols which convey a meaning.

- They tend to be about a product or a company.

- Some logos are so well known that some people could describe or sketch them from memory. For example the Nike logo.

Trademarks

Trademarks are registered symbols of a company. For example Nestlé, Pepsi and Coca Cola produce different products and they use their company name as their trademark. A company that produces a range of products and applies its name as a trademark may develop a strong CORPORATE IDENTITY.

Image

A logo must clearly communicate to the customer what type of product they are selling.

COLOURS

Colours can be used to indicate certain categories of product.

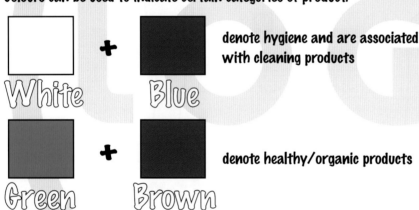

denote hygiene and are associated with cleaning products

denote healthy/organic products

> **TIPS**
> It is important to make sure that your colours and images do not offend minority groups ie. different cultures and religions. Colours and symbols can mean different things to different people. Remember your market research!!

However, in food technology white is often used to denote baking products, while brown represents earth vegetables.

NAME

The brand name (name of the product) is used to tell the customer what the product is about.

For example Cadbury's 'Crunchie' is so named because of the crunchy filling inside the chocolate bar

Pictograms

These are graphic symbols or signs which are used to inform us without the need for words. This means that they take up less space but they do rely on everyone understanding what they mean.

What Typography Is

Typography is the art of letter style and design. There are an amazing number of different letter types available (typefaces). They are often given names based on the designer who created them. Many of them date back to over 400 years ago. Lettering is used to create an effect, a meaning or to make an impact.

Parts Of Letters

A font (letter type) consists of:-
- CAPITAL LETTERS - Also known as 'upper case'
- small letters - Also known as 'lower case'

Letters have basic part names as shown below:

STEM	SERIFS	BAR	CURVE	CONTINUOUS CURVE
P	T	H	G	O
A stroke which runs from top to bottom of the letter	Strokes which finish off the ends of letters	An arm joining two parts together	Any curved shape	A line which shows no join

SERIFS

Serifs are strokes which finish off the ends of stems, arms and curves. Letters without the extra strokes are known as 'SANSERIF'. Serifs come from the use of brushes and chisels. There are four different types of serifs below:-

SANSERIF

SERIF

FULL BRACKETED	HAIRLINE	SLAB	SLAB BRACKETED

Spacing

LETTER SPACING:-

The ease with which text can be read depends on the spaces between the letters. Letters which are close together or far apart can make the text harder to read. Letters on this page have standard spaces between them. But this can be varied for example,   Letters   Letters   L e t t e r s

Sometimes the space between individual letters needs to be adjusted in order to make the word visually evenly spaced. W ATER for example would be adjusted so that the W and A overlap each other's spaces to make the word look visually correct ie. WATER. This process is called **Kerning**.

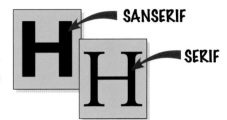

TIPS
Transfer letters come in different styles and sizes and are easy to apply by rubbing over them with a pencil.

WORD SPACING:-

 is the space between words

 the size of a small 'n' is normally used between small letters.

 the size of a large 'O' is normally used between large lettering.

LINE SPACING:- is the space between two consecutive lines of letters. This is also dependent upon the typeface being used.

Introduction

Printing has been used for many years to produce graphic products. There are many factors to take into consideration when choosing the right method of printing your product. Your choice of which method to use is basically determined by the cost, quality and quantity required.

There are FIVE main categories of printing:

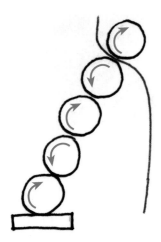

1. RELIEF PRINTING
2. INTAGLIO PRINTING
3. SCREEN PRINTING
4. PLANOGRAPHY PRINTING
5. DRY PRINTING

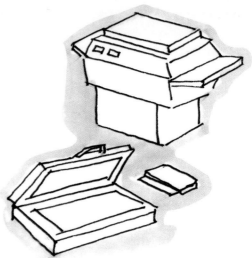

1. Relief Printing

Relief printing is a method in which inked wood, lino or metal has paper pressed onto it to produce a print. The most common types are letterpressing and blockprinting.

LETTERPRESS

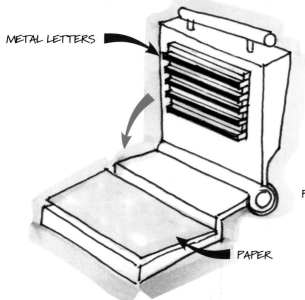

METAL LETTERS

PAPER

BLOCKPRINTING

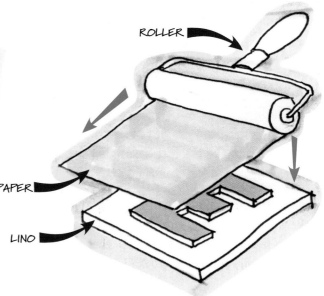

ROLLER

PAPER

LINO

Letterpress prints from a raised surface - often individual pieces of type in a sentence arrangement. The raised surface receives ink and is then pressed onto the paper. This process is expensive as metal letters have to be individually made and a high quality paper is needed to print onto. <u>Letterpress is now only used for high quality books and stationery, generally in short runs.</u>

The image is drawn onto lino, then the lino is cut away from around the image - so that the image sits proud of the surface. You then apply ink to the roller and roll the ink onto your image.

Lastly, the paper is placed on top of the inked image and the pressure from a clean roller presses the paper to the image.

I. Relief Printing (continued)

FLEXOGRAPHY

Flexography is similar to the letterpress process, but instead of using flat printing plates (as in letterpress), this method uses flexible rubber or plastic plates for cylinders. The cylinders rotate to print onto paper, card, plastic or metal. This process is used for packaging, cartons or point of sale material and is often used for long runs at low cost. Below, shows a simple mechanism.

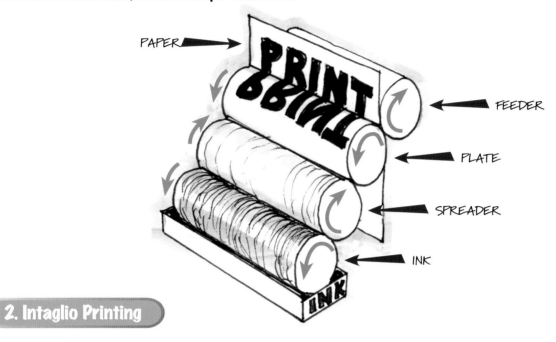

2. Intaglio Printing

GRAVURE

This process must be used for producing high quality prints in large volumes (eg. 500,000 - 1,000,000) as it is very expensive to set up. The gravure plate is made photographically.

● Images are etched onto a plate through a screen. The image is broken into dots.

● Ink fills the 'dot' cells and excess ink is removed using a 'doctor' blade.

● Rubber-covered cylinders press the paper into the cell holes, creating a printed image.
  The deeper the holes, the darker the image.

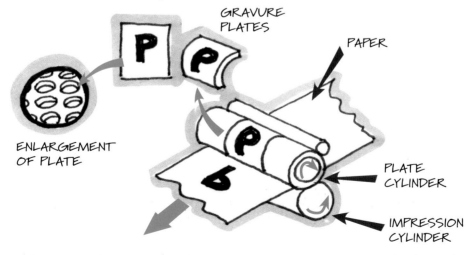

Gravure is used for high quality reproduction of photos, paintings, full colour magazines and books. It can use lighter, cheaper and lower grade papers than lithography. The machines are larger and print at a very high speed. The plates, however, are expensive to make and it is difficult to alter colours.

3. Screen Printing

Screen printing can print designs onto T-shirts, bags, banners, signs, shopping bags, posters, packaging and flyers. Simple stencils can be made and used to produce relatively cheap prints fast and effectively. More sophisticated commercial presses can produce thousands of copies per hour, and produce a good thickness of ink on almost all surfaces.

1

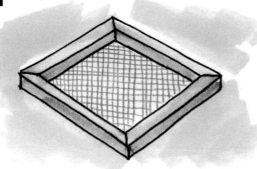

The screen is made as a wooden frame. Nylon fabric is cut 5cm larger than the frame and then stretched and stapled. Gummed tape is stuck around the edge of the frame, to avoid running of ink.

2

The shape is cut out of paper and either part is used to create the stencil. Both parts can be used for background and foreground colours.

3

HINGED FRAME

PAPER TO PRINT ONTO

STENCIL

The screen is hinged to allow it to be raised and lowered without it changing position. The stencil and your paper (or fabric) are placed under the screen.

4

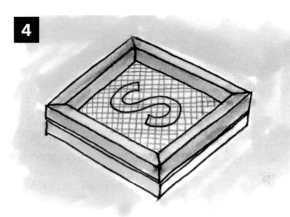

The screen is then lowered and secured in position.

5

Ink is then squeezed through the nylon fabric mesh, by using a rubber-bladed 'squeegee.'

6

The ink then passes through the unblocked area of the stencil to produce your final printed image, when the screen is removed.

4. Planographic Printing

The most common form of Planographic printing is offset lithography, which is mainly used for commercial printing. In this method the image attracts grease (the ink) and rejects water. The areas which aren't being printed on reject the grease and attract water. This method works on the simple principle that water and grease do not mix. The high speed and cheapness of the process makes it the most widely-used method.

LITHOGRAPHY
The best offset litho machines will print in 'full colour' on both sides of the paper in one go. To do this they rely on a 4 colour process using yellow, cyan (a shade of blue), magenta (a shade of red) and black, known as the CYMK process.
Filters are responsible for the COLOUR SEPARATION and a screen converts the separate colours into individual dots which eventually form the final image.

OFFSET LITHOGRAPHY
SINGLE SIDED PRINTING

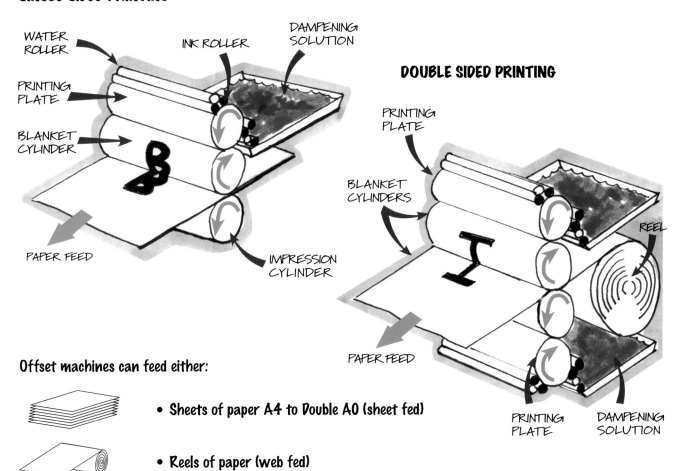

Offset machines can feed either:

- Sheets of paper A4 to Double A0 (sheet fed)

- Reels of paper (web fed)

The process has a printing plate, with the image in relief which is free to rotate. Ink is applied to the printing plate, which is dampened. This repels ink off any non-image areas. The printing plate then transfers an inked image onto the rubber blanket cylinder, which in turn presses the image onto the paper or card as it is fed through.

Small machines often use disposable paper printing plates to print letterheads, business cards and leaflets, in one or two print runs, of up to 5,000 copies. A medium run for larger machines prints between 5,000 - 20,000 copies.

Web fed machines run from a continuous roll of paper, which is cheaper than pre-cut paper.
However, it takes a long time to set the machines up, therefore it is only economical for large print runs.

5. Dry Printing

The general name given to the dry printing process, used by photocopiers and laser printers, is known as XEROGRAPHY.

Photocopiers

In photocopiers the document to be reproduced is placed face down on the glass surface. When illuminated blank parts of the document reflect light onto a positively charged rotation drum. The drum loses its positive charge on all parts where the light hits it. This results in a positive electrostatic image of the document being produced on the drum which corresponds to the dark parts of the document.

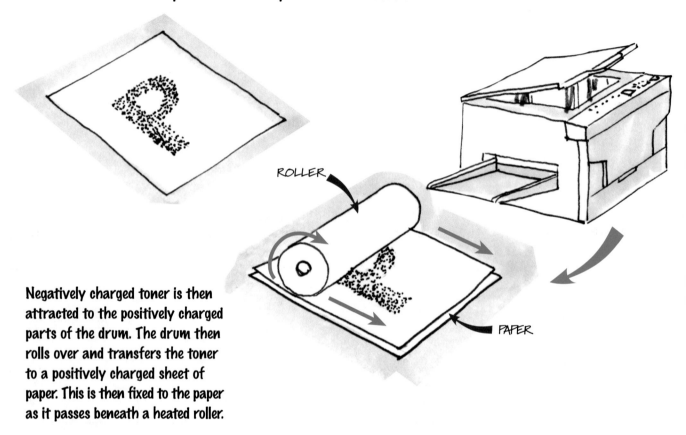

ROLLER

PAPER

Negatively charged toner is then attracted to the positively charged parts of the drum. The drum then rolls over and transfers the toner to a positively charged sheet of paper. This is then fixed to the paper as it passes beneath a heated roller.

Photocopying machines can take copies from books, laser prints and photographs. They have the ability to enlarge or reduce images and can print on both sides of the paper. Advanced photocopiers have the following key features:

- They automatically feed.
- They automatically collate into order.
- They can punch holes.
- They can staple together the required number of copies.
- They can print onto coloured paper, acetate etc.

Laser Printers

Used for one-off and development work they can print work from Computer Aided Design packages onto A4 and A3 paper. They print on a 'WYSIWYG' principle, which stands for 'What You See Is What You Get'. In other words they will print exactly what you see on your screen. Laser printers are low in cost to run and have no set up costs. They also produce a better quality product than ink jet printers, and rely on the same technological principle as the photocopier.

There are many computer systems and peripherals available for use:

Word Processing Packages

The most common package is Microsoft Word and some of the most commonly used tools include:

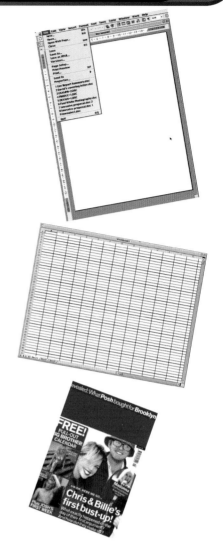

- Standard Features such as SAVE, PRINT, COPY, PASTE etc.
- Text Formatting such as different text, font alignment, italics etc.
- Importing of Graphics eg. clip art
- Mail Merge where letters can be personalised from a database.

Spreadsheets

A program that enables information to be arranged onto a grid, within a range of cells. This enables the user to quickly assess the effect of varying one of the pieces of information on the project as a whole eg. cost. It is also capable of interpreting the information as different types of charts and graphs.

Desktop Publishing Packages

These are often used for magazines, newspapers and leaflets as this gives more control over the layout of a page. A common package is Microsoft Publisher, where pictures and text can be laid out on a page with images imported from other software and clip art libraries.

Graphic Packages

- Painting Packages These allow freehand drawing and colouring to be done. Images are made up of tiny dots called PIXELS and are stored as bitmap images. This program also allows you to work in finer detail but it can use up a lot of memory.

- Drawing Packages can be attached to a Microsoft package to enable you to draw with lines and shapes. Uses up less memory than painting packages.

- CAD (Computer Aided Design) Sophisticated drawing packages used by designers, engineers and architects to produce detailed drawings. The advantages of CAD are:

 objects can be drawn with great accuracy and scaled, rotated or reflected.

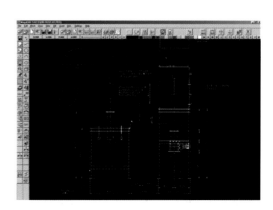

 drawings can be created in 3D and viewed from any angle.

 can simulate how a product can perform without using expensive testing methods.

 can store lots of information, therefore saving on office space.

The Internet

The World Wide Web (www) is the most common feature of the internet. To connect to the internet you need the following devices: a computer, phone line, a modem or ISDN connection, an ISP (Internet Service Provider) and browser software.

- www The World Wide Web stores millions of web pages on web servers.
- HTML (Hypertext Markup Language) is the language, or code, of web pages.
- Website This is a set of web pages created by an organisation.
- Surfing Moving around the internet by using a program which enables you to read the pages at different sites eg. Netscape or Internet Explorer.
- Search Engine Used to search the net for a particular topic, possibly using Yahoo, Excite, Lycos, Ask Jeeves etc.
- E-mail (Electronic Mail) Worldwide communication at the cost of a local phone call.

Computer Input Devices

These allow data to be entered into a computer.
- Barcodes Vertical bars in different groups read by an optical scanner. Printed on almost everything you buy now, as they are durable and cheap to produce.
- Concept Keyboard Grid of buttons on a flat board, which contains information and a description or picture on each button. Used commonly on fast food tills.
- Graphics Tablet A flat pad, where the designer uses a special pen to create an accurate image on the screen.
- Scanner A cheap way of transferring images onto the computer.
- Digital Camera Stores a digital photographic image which is read by computer.

ISBN 1-903068-43-6

9 781903 068434

Computer Output Devices

These allow information to be downloaded to the user in the form of a 'hard' copy.
- Ink-jet Printers Generally cheap to buy although quality and speed levels are a drawback.
- Laser Printers Produce very good quality prints. More expensive than ink-jet printers.
- Plotters Used for A3, or bigger, size drawings. Used mainly in conjunction with CAD and CAM applications. Output is accurate and of very good quality.

CAM (Computer Aided Manufacture)

This is the manufacture of products using computerised machines.
The computers control the movement of the machines by issuing a set of instructions.
More and more manufacturing processes in industry are using computerised machines, for the following reasons:

 computers make fewer mistakes, if they are properly programmed.

 increased productivity as they can carry on continuously.

 less human labour is required as computers do not get tired!

 the standard of manufacture is very reliable and consistent.

 robots can undertake tasks which could be considered unsafe for humans to handle.

Using a computer for your coursework, could improve both the quality and accuracy of your work. Computerised equipment could be used in the following areas of the design process.

DESIGN IDEAS

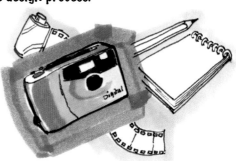

- Take pictures of existing products using a digital camera. Then, by using compatible software you can adjust the existing products, as a starting point for your ideas.

- Alternatively use a computer aided design package to produce graphic ideas quickly.

DEVELOPMENT

- Use the internet, a database or a CD-ROM to obtain the best or most suitable material for your design.

- If your school has the facilities, you can make mock-ups/models of your design using a CAM (Computer Aided Manufacture) machine.

FINAL DESIGN

- You could scan your final presentation drawing and use graphics from a publishing package, to produce a professional looking presentation or an advertisement for your product.

- You could use the digital camera to photograph your final prototype (model), to achieve the same result as above.

PLANNING

- Use Microsoft Word to produce flow diagrams, of a stage by stage process eg. how to make your model (plan of manufacture).

- Use spreadsheets eg. Microsoft Excel, to work out detailed costings for your final product.

MAKING

Your final product could be made via Computer Aided Manufacture (CAM). Thin vinyl (plastic) can be cut out by a CAM cutter. The design could be produced via a computer aided design package and transferred to self-adhesive film.

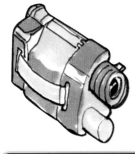

EVALUATION

- A video presentation could be a way to show your ideas and how they work. It can record any testing, which is difficult to record on paper. Videos can be connected to the computer.

- A report is essential and should be written in detail on a word processing package.

INDUSTRIAL APPLICATION OF CAD/CAM

Computers can deal with work more efficiently, both when a product is being designed or is in production. They utilise both CAD (Computer Aided Design) and CAM (Computer Aided Manufacture) Systems. For example, when a jacket is produced, there are, typically, 7 stages across the CAD and CAM Systems.

Computer Aided Design

In the first stage the cost of fabric, labour and materials must be researched. Improvements should be made on previous garments or styles and market research material utilised. As well as helping with these the computer can assist with productivity, coordination, development and management of styles.

At this stage, the jacket design will be completed, sizes will be modified and scaled correctly (for example a ladies' size 14 will increase in exact proportion to a size 12) and any final design changes will be made.

Each separate part (ie. front sleeve, rear sleeve, left back, right back etc.) can be drawn on the computer and then placed in the most economical way, to reduce waste.

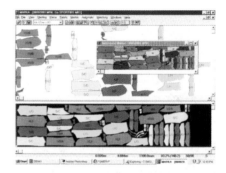

Any customised tailoring orders could be dealt with at this stage. This would involve measuring the customer exactly (ie. chest, shoulders etc.) and then producing a product specifically designed and measured to fit her.

Computer Aided Manufacture

It is essential that patterns match (eg. the pattern of the fabric must be continuous across the back of the jacket). Both fabric and time must be used economically.

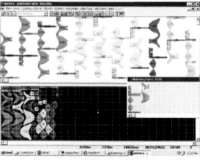

The pieces which have been marked out on the computer are drawn onto the fabric ready for cutting. This should be done in the minimum time, with the minimum cost and minimum wastage.

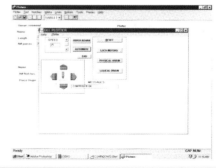

The fabric is cut. A computerised machine could be used, which would reduce the need for individual cutters and so reduce staffing costs.

* Many thanks to Geoffrey E. Macpherson Ltd, Nottingham
for permission to reproduce these photographs.

Introduction

A mechanism creates movement within a product - there will be occasions when you need to apply a mechanism to a product; whether it be a moving sign or a board game.

There are four types of movement ...

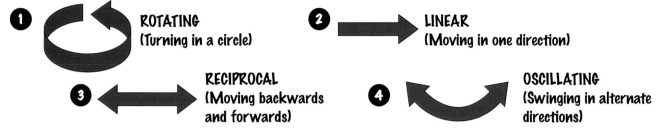

1 ROTATING (Turning in a circle)

2 LINEAR (Moving in one direction)

3 RECIPROCAL (Moving backwards and forwards)

4 OSCILLATING (Swinging in alternate directions)

Mechanisms can be split into two sections:-

1. GENERAL MECHANICAL MOVEMENT
2. CARD MECHANISMS

General Mechanical Movement

The following theory will help you to understand how the basic elements of mechanisms work.
It is also important to look at existing products and work out what mechanisms are involved to make them move. This will help when you begin to develop your design ideas, so that you can take an existing method and build the visual graphic around it.

LEVERS 1 - BASIC PRINCIPLES

All machines will almost certainly have at least one lever. A lever is a simple device, consisting of a rigid bar which pivots about a fixed point. This point is called the 'fulcrum'.

- A 'load' is applied at one end of a 'rigid bar'. The bar is placed centrally on top of the 'fulcrum' (pivot point).
- At the other end of the bar, a force is applied - called the 'effort'.
- This results in a single 'lever' movement about the pivot point.

EXAMPLE OF LEVERS 1

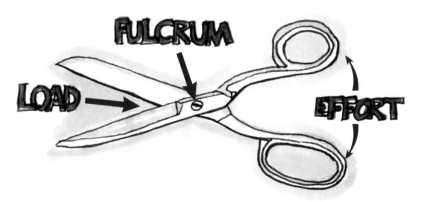

A pair of scissors is an example of a simple lever system.
- The EFFORT:- is applied by the hands at one end.
- The LOAD:- is the resistance against the cutting edge.
- The FULCRUM:- is the screw which holds the two halves together and allows for movement.

More effort is applied when cutting thicker paper or card, than when cutting thin paper.

LEVERS 2 - FORCE MULTIPLIERS

By altering the position of the fulcrum, the effort can be multiplied and therefore lift a larger load.

The leverage of the blue and yellow sections on the rigid bar, are now at a ratio of 6:2 or 3:1.

- So an effort of 1 could move a load of 3, but the effort end will have to move 3 times further than the load 'end.'

EXAMPLE OF LEVERS 2

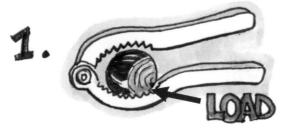

Nutcrackers are an example of how a lever can be used to act as a force multiplier. In this case, the load is closer to the fulcrum than the effort, resulting in more force being applied.

LEVERS 3 - MOVEMENT MULTIPLIERS

The third type of lever, is where the effort is applied between the load and the fulcrum. The effort needed is greater than the load, but this time the amount of movement is multiplied.

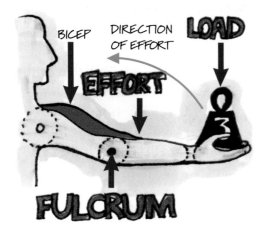

EXAMPLE OF LEVERS 3

The elbow is the fulcrum. The effort is provided by the biceps muscle, which attaches to the forearm just below the elbow. A relatively small movement of the biceps results in a relatively large movement of the end of the lower arm, but the effort needs to be greater than the load.

Cranks and cams are relatively simple devices which convert...
... ROTARY MOTION to LINEAR MOTION (or vice versa).

Cranks

Cranks can convert linear movement to rotary
movement in the case of the tricycle and child's
pedal car. The crankshaft in an automobile also does
this. Arranged differently, the crank can convert
rotary motion to linear motion. This could be used
to drive a pump for instance.

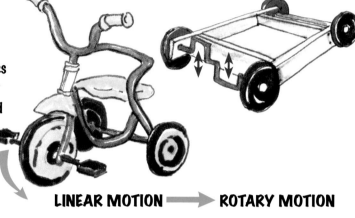

LINEAR MOTION ⟶ ROTARY MOTION

ROTARY   **LINEAR**

Cams

A cam is a device which converts one type of movement into another. The example below shows a ROTARY CAM
which converts ROTARY MOTION into RECIPROCATING MOTION (up and down movement ↕) in the cam follower.
This motion can be varied by using different shaped cams.

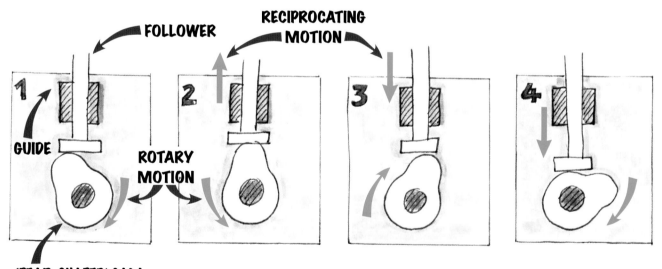

FOLLOWER   **RECIPROCATING MOTION**

ROTARY MOTION

1 **GUIDE**   **2**   **3**   **4**

'PEAR-SHAPED' CAM

- A FOLLOWER is a rod which moves up and down. This will have an object of your choice on top.
- A GUIDE holds the FOLLOWER in place.

This is how the
simple cam looks
in 3D

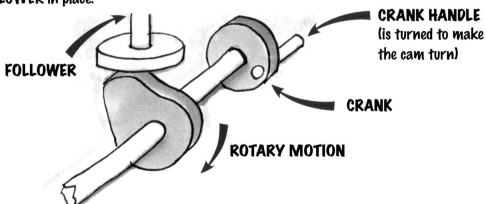

FOLLOWER

CRANK HANDLE
(is turned to make
the cam turn)

CRANK

ROTARY MOTION

Springs

There are lots of different types of spring which are used in a variety of ways to resist different forces. They can be placed into four broad groups ...

1
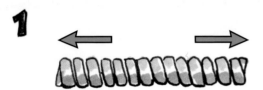

Springs which resist ...
... EXTENSION

2

Springs which resist ...
... COMPRESSION

3

Springs which resist ...
... RADIAL MOVEMENT

4

Springs which resist ...
... TWISTING

The springs shown are the large kind used in resistant materials but the same principles can be applied in graphical products by using certain types of modern plastics.

Linkages

Sometimes a linkage can act as a lever, but most times it transfers one mechanical motion to another. It is often used to connect cams to cranks or cams to levers or vice versa. Below are three simple linkage examples. A simple example, with which you may be familiar, is a metal tool box which opens to reveal different levels of trays.

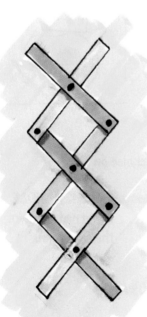

TONGS
LINKAGE

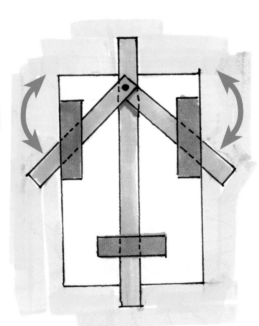

MOVING WINGS
LINKAGE

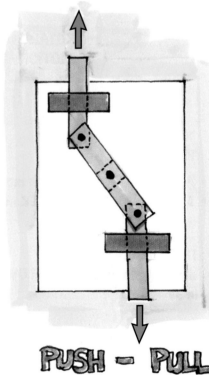

PUSH – PULL
LINKAGE

Gears

Gears are like linkages, transferring one motion to another. Gear wheels have teeth around the edge which mesh with the teeth of another gear. Gear wheels may also be linked by chains or belts. Gears are used as force multipliers or reducers to make things go faster or slower. They are used on bikes and in cars; also in hand whisks, salad spinners, toys and bottle openers.

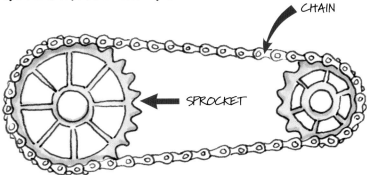

- Gears can reduce the applied force needed to cycle uphill by increasing the rate at which you have to pedal.

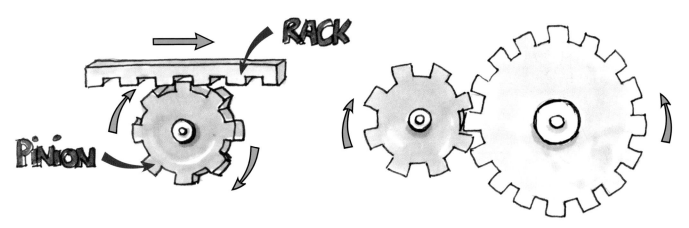

- A rack and pinion linkage can be used in cars to convert the rotary motion of the steering wheel into a lateral movement of the wheels.

- The pinion moves the big wheel.
  The big wheel has twice as many teeth therefore rotates at half the speed (but with twice the force).

Pulleys

A pulley is a wheel with a groove around it through which runs a belt. They are used to control how fast something turns. Pulleys are also used to make lifting easier. Other examples of pulleys are in cassette recorders, washing machines and cranes. In reality these are less frequently in graphical products.

1. This drive incorporates gearing - the big wheel rotates more slowly than the small wheel, but with greater force.

2. A twist in the belt (pulley) makes the wheels turn in the opposite direction.

Card Mechanisms

Card and paper can be used for mechanisms for greetings cards, packaging and POS (Point-Of-Sale) displays. Paper and card can be bought in different colours, weights, textures and thicknesses. For pop-ups on card, thin cardboard can be used. For POS displays, heavy weight or corrugated cardboard must be used.

SCORING

You need to score the card or paper in order to make it easier and neater to fold. Use a metal safety ruler to score a craft knife or a scalpel against. (Remember to keep your fingers out of the way!)

FOLDING

To create a neater fold, hold the metal ruler against the fold.

1. V Fold Mechanisms

glue tabs

Fold

This is a simple fold.
Glue is applied underneath the tabs.
The centre of the 'V' is lined-up with the fold of the card.

1. 90°
- Card will stand up vertically when opened.

2. 60°
- Card will lean backwards when opened.

3. 100°
- Card will lean forwards when opened.

2. Rotary Mechanisms

This mechanism gives a circular or rotating motion.

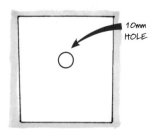

10mm HOLE

Make a 10mm hole in the card.

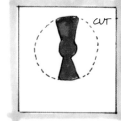

CUT

On another piece draw a 30mm circle and draw a tab to cut out.

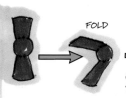

FOLD   GLUE TO SURFACE

Glue folded tab to shape of propeller.

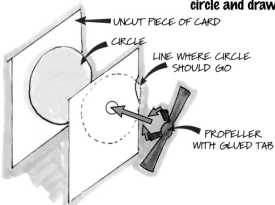

UNCUT PIECE OF CARD

CIRCLE

LINE WHERE CIRCLE SHOULD GO

PROPELLER WITH GLUED TAB

- Push the red tabs through the hole and glue to the yellow circle.

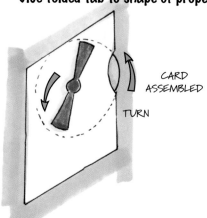

CARD ASSEMBLED

TURN

- Glue the two pieces of card together around the perimeter

3. Incised Mechanisms

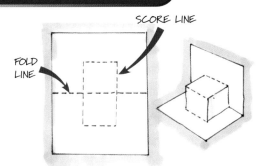

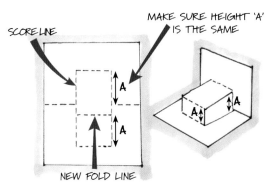

Score lines from one piece of card. The lines should be parallel and the fold line is in the centre.

This is the same principle as the previous incised mechanism - only the fold line has moved to create a different shape.

4. Sliding Mechanisms

1 Cut a slot.

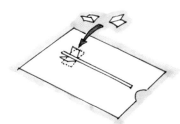

2 Fold two small strips of card - to be fed through the slot on stage 4.

3 Cut a strip of card longer than the length of your card.

Glue small folded strips of card to the long strip and feed through the slot in the card.

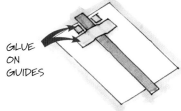

5 Attach guides.

6 Glue image to small pieces of card.

5. Layer Mechanisms

Creating more than one layer, using strips of card and tabs.

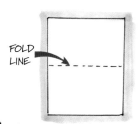

1 Score and fold your card.

2 Make a smaller piece with tabs.

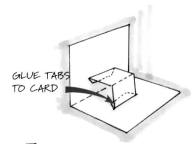

3 Glue one to the other.

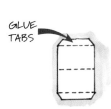

4 Make a smaller piece of card with a fold and 2 glue tabs.

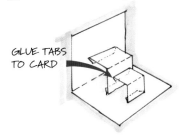

5 Glue this smaller piece to the front of the bigger piece of card.

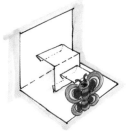

6 You can then glue pictures to the front.

Product analysis is looking at a product, disassembling the product (taking it apart) and working out how it was made. By looking carefully at a product you are not only evaluating it but learning from it too.

How To Analyse A Product

The following list gives categories of study for your chosen product and can be used as a guideline when analysing a product.

1. FUNCTION

What is the need for this product? Use diagrams to demonstrate how it is used and to explain its purpose, for example ...

- Two functions include:- eating with breakfast or as a drink. Gives calcium to strengthen bones.

2. COST

How much does the product cost, either individually or in bulk?

1 PINT =£0.40

2 PINTS =£0.70

(prices are approximate)

3. TARGET MARKET

Who uses this product and how do you know? (A questionnaire is a good idea!) Are different styles used for different age groups, cultures and religions?

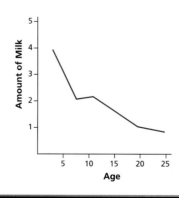

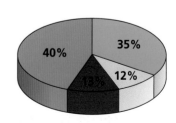

- Use line graphs, bar charts, pie charts and pictographs to record results - and analyse these!

4. HISTORY

Where does the product originate from? Use diagrams to explain (using dates/events where possible) the evolution of the product.

For example:

The example shows drawings only - you will need more information eg. dates etc ...

5. ALTERNATIVE PRODUCTS

Evaluate your product against either a similar or a competitive product. How do they compare on price, shape, form, use etc ...

Here is a comparison of a carton against a plastic container.

- Packaging is difficult to open.
- Can be easily thrown away with household rubbish.
- Can be recycled.

- Bulky in transportation.
- Easy to open and reseal.
- Can be reused for other purposes (but not for food products) and recycled.

6. ERGONOMICS

How does your product suit the user?
Use Anthropometric data to help and discuss (using diagrams) how the user uses the product.

- Look at how the hand grips the handle on the bottle. You will need to describe this.

- Describe how the bottle top is taken off.

- When pouring, how heavy is it to lift and which parts of the body enable this function to happen.

7. HYGIENE

Is the product easy to clean? Use comparisons with other similar products.

8. MANUFACTURING PROCESS

What method of production is used to make your product? Explain, using diagrams, why this method is used.

EXAMPLE OF A BLOW MOULDING PROCESS, FOR A CONTAINER

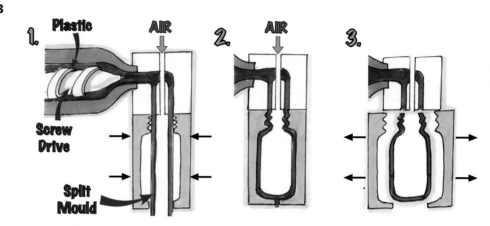

1.
Plastic
AIR
Screw Drive
Split Mould

2.
AIR

3.

9. MATERIALS

What material(s) is your product made from?
What are the origins and properties of each material and why is that material used?
Yet again, compare against another similar product.

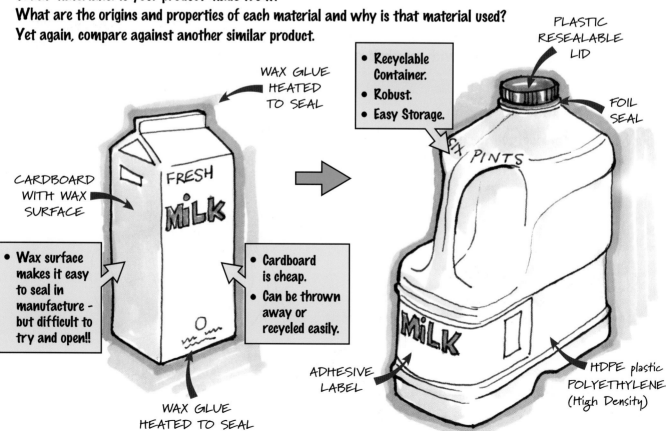

WAX GLUE HEATED TO SEAL

CARDBOARD WITH WAX SURFACE

FRESH MiLK

- Wax surface makes it easy to seal in manufacture – but difficult to try and open!!

- Cardboard is cheap.
- Can be thrown away or recycled easily.

WAX GLUE HEATED TO SEAL

- Recyclable Container.
- Robust.
- Easy Storage.

PLASTIC RESEALABLE LID

FOIL SEAL

SIX PINTS

MiLK

ADHESIVE LABEL

HDPE plastic POLYETHYLENE (High Density)

Other Factors To Consider

RECYCLED MATERIALS

How can your product be recycled?
Is it a danger to the environment?
Will it cause any pollution?
You should take into account whether your product is made
from renewable or non-renewable materials.

SAFETY

Is your product safe? What safety features does it have?
Is it safe for children to use - what considerations have been made?

MARKETING

How is your product marketed, promoted and sold? Magazine, newspaper adverts,
point of sale stands, TV, posters or leaflets (give examples and proof). Compare how
your product is marketed with a similar or competitive product.

AESTHETICS

What makes your product look good?
Look at shape/form/symmetry/colour etc.

MASS OR BATCH PRODUCTION

What quantities is the product made in?

It is important to choose the right material for your product. Here are some basic considerations to take into account:-

1. Do the properties of the material meet your specifications?

2. What is the cheapest material you could use which would still meet the specifications?

3. How durable is the material you could use? How long will it last?

4. What type of finishes can you achieve for your chosen material?

Plastics

Plastics are manufactured using a process known as POLYMERISATION. Polymerisation occurs when MONOMERS join together to form long chains of molecules called POLYMERS.

MONOMERS   POLYMERISATION   POLYMER

Polymerisation is derived from the word POLY which means 'many' and MER which means 'part', so, for example...

POLYSTYRENE is made up of single monomers of STYRENE, joined together to form a long chain.

<u>There are two different types of plastic:</u>

1. THERMOSETTING PLASTICS

Thermosetting plastics are heated and moulded into shape. If re-heated they cannot soften as the monomers are interlinked. Individual monomers are joined together to form a massive polymer.

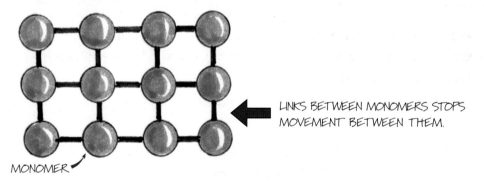

LINKS BETWEEN MONOMERS STOPS MOVEMENT BETWEEN THEM.

MONOMER

2. THERMOPLASTICS

Thermoplastics will soften when they are heated, and can be shaped when hot. The plastic will harden when it is cooled, but can be reshaped if heated up again. This means that thermoplastics are RECYCLABLE.

NO LINKS BETWEEN MONOMERS

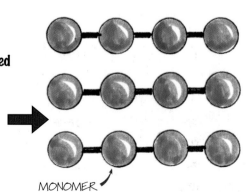

MONOMER

NAME AND DESCRIPTION		USES
MELAMINE FORMALDEHYDE (MELAMINE METHANAL MF) Heat resistant polymer		Tableware, electrical installations, synthetic resin paints, decorative laminates, worktops.
EPOXY RESIN (EPOXIDE, ER) A resin and a hardener mixed to produce a cast.		Castings, printed circuit boards (PCB's), surface coating.
POLYESTER RESIN (PR) Polymerises at room temperature, a resin and hardener mixed together. Often reinforced with GLASS FIBRE.		Laminated to form GRP (Glass Reinforced Plastic) castings, encapsulations, car bodies, boats.
PHENOL FORMALDEHYDE (PHENOL METHANAL, PF) (BAKELITE) Hard, brittle plastic with dark colour, glossy finish. Resists heat.		Dark coloured electrical fittings and parts for domestic appliances, bottle tops, kettle/iron/saucepan handles.
UREA FORMALDEHYDE A colourless polymer - coloured with artificial pigments to produce a wide range of different colours.		Door Handles, cupboard handles, bottle tops, electrical switches, electrical fittings.

NAME AND DESCRIPTION		USES
POLYTHENE (HIGH DENSITY) HDPE Stiff, strong plastic. Softens at between 120-130°C.		Pipes, bowls, milk crates, buckets.
POLYTHENE (LOW DENSITY) LDPE Weaker and softer and more flexible than HDPE. Softens at 85°C.		Packaging, film, carrier bags, toys, 'squeezy' detergent bottles.
POLYPROPYLENE (PP) High impact strength, softens at 150°C - can be flexed many times without breaking.		Bottle crates, medical equipment, syringes, food containers, boxes, nets, storage.
POLYSTYRENE (PS) (expanded) Soft and spongy - good heat insulating properties. Low density - good at absorbing shock.		Packaging, sound and heat insulation, ceiling tiles.
NYLON Hard material - good resistance to wear and tear. Solid nylon has low friction qualities and a high melting point.		Curtain rail fittings, combs, hinges, bearings, clothes, gear wheels.
PVC, rigid (polyvinyl chloride) Stiff, hard wearing. Plasticiser can be added to create a softer more rubbery material.		Air and water pipes, chemical tanks, shoe soles, shrink and blister packaging. Floor and wall covering.
ACRYLIC (POLYMETHYL - METHACRYLATE) Trade name - Perspex. Glass-like transparency or opaque - can be coloured with pigments. Hard wearing, will not shatter.		Display signs, baths, roof lights, machine guards.

Injection Moulding

Typical Materials used in this process are: POLYTHENE, POLYSTYRENE, POLYPROPYLENE and NYLON.

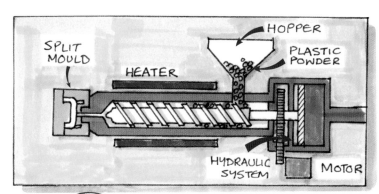

- Plastic powder or granules are fed from the hopper into a hollow steel barrel.

- The heaters melt the plastic as the screw moves it along towards the mould.

- Once sufficient melted plastic has accumulated, the hydraulic system forces the plastic into the mould.

- Pressure is maintained on the mould, until it has cooled enough to be opened.

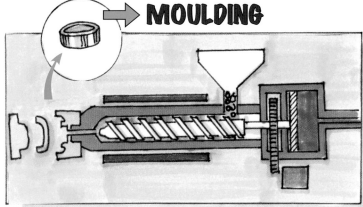

Extrusion

Typical materials used in this process are POLYTHENE, PVC and NYLON.

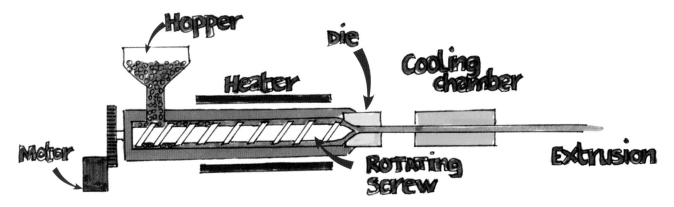

- Plastic granules are fed into the hopper by the rotating screw.

- The plastic granules are heated as they are fed through .

- The difference between the injection moulding process and the extrusion process, is that the softened plastic is forced through a die in a continuous stream, to create long tube or sectional extrusions.

- The extrusions are then passed through a cooling chamber.

Blow Moulding

Common materials used are PVC, POLYTHENE and POLYPROPYLENE.
This process is the same as the EXTRUSION process, apart from the air supply and a split mould instead of the cooling chamber.

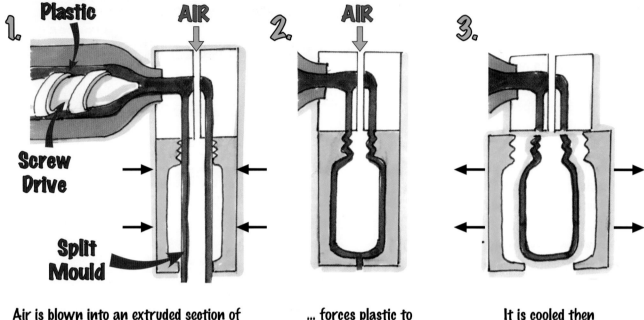

Air is blown into an extruded section of tube, where it expands and ...

... forces plastic to the sides of the mould.

It is cooled then opened to remove the product.

Compression Moulding

PHENOL, UREA AND MELAMINE FORMALDEHYDE are materials used in this process.
• A large force is used to squash a cube of polymer into a heated mould.
• The cube of polymer is in the form of a powder, known as a 'slug'.
• Compression moulding is used with THERMOSETTING PLASTICS.

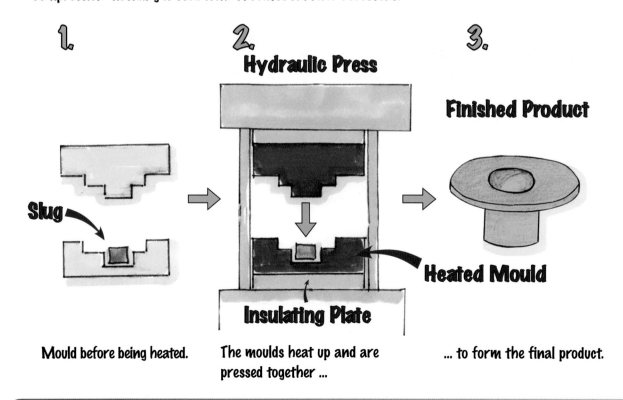

Mould before being heated.

The moulds heat up and are pressed together ...

... to form the final product.

This process can be used as an alternative to INJECTION or BLOW moulding. Mould costs are very much cheaper, (by up to 90%). It is easier to make alterations to a rotational mould, cutting down the development time in manufacture. A rotational mould machine has three arms fixed at the same point. Moulds would be attached to each arm and rotated continuously with thermoplastic powder.

● Used to make footballs, road cones and storage tanks.
● Mouldings are made from POLYTHENE (PE) - which has fire retardant and vandal resistant qualities.

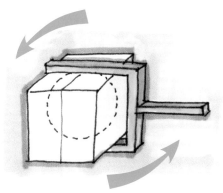

A two piece mould attached to an arm, which enables it to rotate.

1

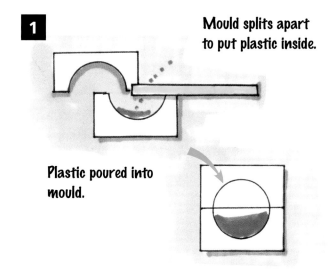

Mould splits apart to put plastic inside.

Plastic poured into mould.

2

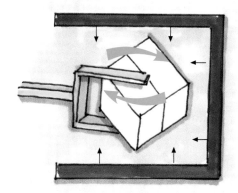

Heat is applied while the mould is rotated. Plastic is thrown to the inner surface of the mould.

3

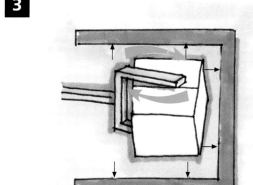

It continues to rotate until finally the mould is allowed to cool.

4

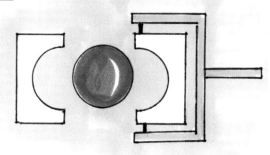

The mould is opened up and the product is ejected.

SECTION OF FINAL PRODUCT

Vacuum Forming

This technique uses thermoplastic materials in the form of sheets which can measure up to 1.5m x 1.8m. Perhaps the most popular material is POLYSTYRENE which is cheap and easy to form. Basically the process relies on 'sucking' heated plastic onto the shape of mould that is required.

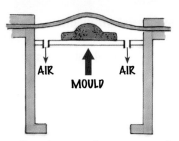

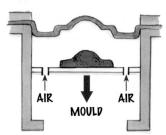

- The plastic is heated and the mould moves close to it.
- Air is 'sucked out' to form a vacuum.

- Removing the air causes the hot plastic to be sucked onto the mould.
- As the temperature of the plastic falls, a rigid impression of the mould is formed.

- The vacuum pump is turned off, allowing air to enter
- The mould is lowered, separating it from the final product.

Line Bending

SAFETY TIP
Keep your fingers away from the heat element and always remember to switch off after use.

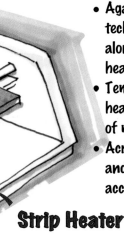

Strip Heater

- Again, thermoplastic sheets are used in this technique, but this time they are heated only along the line of the intended fold, by a special heating element.
- Temperature switches control the amount of heat produced to cater for different thicknesses of material.
- Acrylic sheets are often used for this process, and bending jigs can be used to produce accurate angles, and shapes.

JIG

Calendering

This is the most common method of manufacturing single ply membranes, fabrics and wallpapers. PVC and cellulose acetate are the materials most commonly used. The process involves pulling the raw material through pressure rollers to produce a finished sheet material.

- The distance between the NIP ROLLERS is adjusted to produce the desired thickness of material.
- A roller temperature of between 160°C and 220°C is required for PVC.
- 'Embossing Rollers' can also be used to produce a pattern on the fabric.

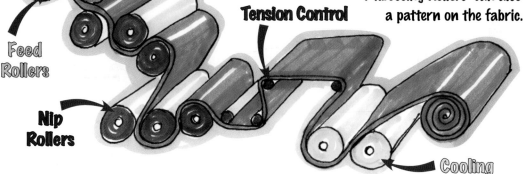

Tension Control

Feed Rollers

Nip Rollers

Cooling Rollers

A plan of manufacture is a stage-by-stage plan of how your product is to be made. Your plan should ...

... be split into a number of different stages.

... name all the right processes, in the correct order.

... list all the correct tools to be used.

... suggest an estimated time scale for each stage.

... suggest actions to take when things go wrong.

The flow-diagram below suggests basic stages to include. These may alter according to the type of product that you intend to produce.

PLAN OF MANUFACTURE SCHEDULE

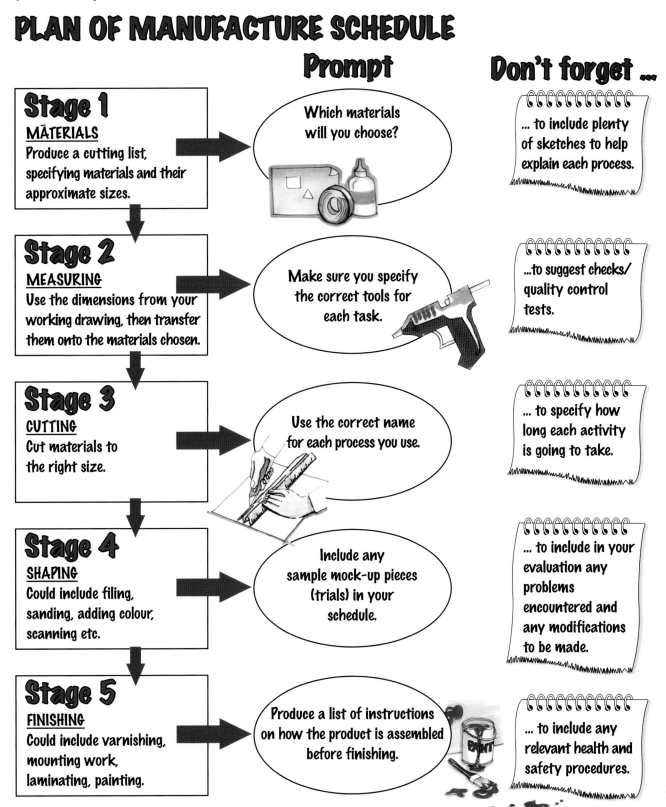

Prompt

Don't forget ...

Stage 1

MATERIALS

Produce a cutting list, specifying materials and their approximate sizes.

Which materials will you choose?

... to include plenty of sketches to help explain each process.

Stage 2

MEASURING

Use the dimensions from your working drawing, then transfer them onto the materials chosen.

Make sure you specify the correct tools for each task.

...to suggest checks/ quality control tests.

Stage 3

CUTTING

Cut materials to the right size.

Use the correct name for each process you use.

... to specify how long each activity is going to take.

Stage 4

SHAPING

Could include filing, sanding, adding colour, scanning etc.

Include any sample mock-up pieces (trials) in your schedule.

... to include in your evaluation any problems encountered and any modifications to be made.

Stage 5

FINISHING

Could include varnishing, mounting work, laminating, painting.

Produce a list of instructions on how the product is assembled before finishing.

... to include any relevant health and safety procedures.

Flow Chart Symbols

A flow chart shows the order in which a series of tasks are carried out, in other words the sequence of events in which something is produced. There are different, specific symbols for each stage of the process. Some of these are shown below.

TERMINATOR
represents start, restart, stop.

DECISION
represents a choice which can lead to another pathway.

PROCESS
represents a particular instruction or action.

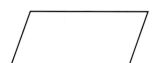

INPUT/OUTPUT
represents additions to or removals from the particular process.

The symbols are linked together by arrows which indicate the correct sequence of events. The aim should be to make the flow chart as clear and simple as possible.

An Example Of A Simple Flow Chart

In this example the flow chart identifies the stages in the process of making several copies of a document using a photocopier ...

This flow chart incorporates a feedback loop which enables the print density to be controlled.
If the first copy was too dark you would return to stage 1 and adjust the toner. If the next copy was too pale you would again return to stage 1 and adjust the toner until the copy you produced was suitable.

Clearly, this simple example could be expanded to take into account the size of the copies, or whether they are printed on both sides etc. In complicated manufacturing processes several flow charts can be used to represent different stages of manufacture, this makes the whole process easier to follow.

When you use flow charts to describe a process, make sure that they are completely unambiguous, ie. they should only be able to be interpreted in one way. Test them thoroughly to ensure that they are "idiot-proof".

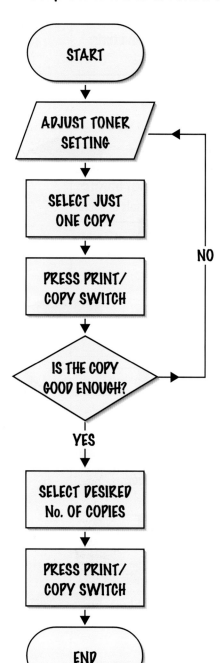

Although you will only manufacture one final product from your design it is important that you are aware of the various possible methods of production and how yours could be produced commercially.

'One-off' Production

This is when one product is made at ...
... one particular time.
It could be a prototype or a very intricate object.
'One-off' production usually takes a long time ...
... which very often results in the product being expensive.
A typical product could be a display for an exhibition stand.

Batch Production

A series of products (which are all the same) ...
... are made together in either small or large quantities.
Once made, another series of products may be ...
... produced using the same equipment and workforce.
A typical product could be a business card.

Mass Production

This involves the product going through various stages ...
... on a production line where the workers at a ...
... particular stage are responsible for a certain part of the product.
It usually involves the product being produced for days, ...
... even weeks and in large numbers.
This sort of production results in the product being relatively inexpensive ..
... but production could be halted if a problem occurs at any stage of the production line.
A typical product could be a fancy chocolate box or car assembly.

Continuous Production

This is where the product is continually produced ...
... over a period of hours, days even years.
This sort of production very often results ...
... in the product being relatively inexpensive.
A typical product could be a milk carton.

'Just In Time' Production

This involves the arrival of component parts ...
... at exactly, the time they are needed at the factory.
'Just in time' allows for less storage space ...
... saving on costly warehousing.
However, if the supply of components is stopped, ...
... the production line stops which then becomes very costly.

Quality Control

Quality Control is a series of checks which are carried out on a product as it is made. The checks are made to make sure that each product meets a specific standard. Some likely tests to be carried out on the product involve ...

SIZE

WEIGHT

COLOUR

FORM

Testing is an important part of the manufacture of a product, and it can take place anytime during production. For example, an injection moulded bottle top could be tested after ten, a thousand or a million of them have been produced. In this particular example some of the tests done would include: checking its diameter, its thickness and whether it screws properly onto its container. As every object cannot be guaranteed to accurately meet the specifications when produced in large quantities, a tolerance has to be applied. This specifies the allowed minimum and maximum measurements. Analysis of tolerance tests can signal the imminent failure of a machine and can help to achieve the ultimate aim of quality control which is ZERO FAULTS.

OUTSIDE DIAMETER

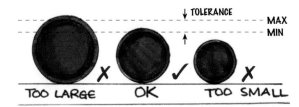
↓ TOLERANCE — MAX — MIN
TOO LARGE ✗   OK ✓   TOO SMALL ✗

Quality control in printed products is aided by the use of ...

a) **COLOUR BARS** (1)
Which are used to check the consistency and density of colours on each page.

b) **REGISTRATION MARKS** (2)
These ensure that the colours are correctly aligned and should appear black when viewed using a magnifying glass.

c) **VISUAL CHECKS**
To ensure that there are no breaks in the typeface and all text is clear and legible.

CY
Y
C
(1)

⊕ (2)

QUALITY CONTRO

Quality Control

Quality Control is a series of make sure that each product

Quality Assurance

Quality Assurance checks the systems which make the products, before, during and after manufacture. It ensures that consistency is achieved and that the product is of the required standard. Factors such as equipment, materials, processes and staff training need to be constantly monitored.

QUALITY ASSURANCE
Before — **During** — **After**
MAKING

TIPS
Make sure that you recognise symbols and signs relating to quality assurance, that are endorsed by recognised authorities.

Non-Destructive And Destructive Testing Of A Product

NON-DESTRUCTIVE - Tests are made to ensure that the product works, without causing any damage.

DESTRUCTIVE - A sample of products are made to be tested for their strength; they will be tested until they are damaged or completely broken.

An evaluation is a review of your final product, using your judgement to assess the outcome of the design. A good place to start would be to answer the following questions:

1. Do you find your product easy to use?

2. Does it function in the way that it was intended to?

3. What do you think of the final outcome? Do you like or dislike it? Explain why.

4. Would you purchase it?

5. What are your design's main advantages and disadvantages?

Another way to evaluate is to test your product and record the results of the test.

Specifications

The next stage would be to check whether or not you have fulfilled your list of specifications. A simple method would be to produce a table, which either questions or tests each specification:-

EXAMPLE:

SPECIFICATION	TEST OR QUESTION	RESULT AND EVALUATION COMMENT
SIZE	**TEST** • Measure your product and compare against your original sizes. **QUESTION** • Have you managed to keep within your size range?	If you produced different sizes for your product, explain why and what alterations you had to make.
DURABILITY	**TEST** • DESTRUCTIVE - drop product on the floor, from 1 metre above floor level. **QUESTION** • How long will it last?	Did your product withstand the pressure or force you inflicted upon it? If it did - what does that tell you? If it didn't, explain the possible modifications you could make to increase durability.

The following list is a guideline to the type of questions you could answer, in relation to each specification. (Your specifications will vary according to the product you have designed; therefore the following are merely suggested for consideration.)

1.

Weight/Size

Does the weight affect the way your product functions?
Is it easily transportable?

2.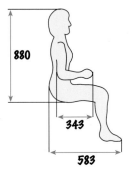

Ergonomics

Is it easy to use?
How does it affect its environment?
How is it affected by its environment?
How is the product used?

3.

Safety

How safe is the design?
Who is it safe for?
Is it safe for children to use?

4.

Cost

Did you stay within your budget? Don't try to cost in terms of pounds but in a comparative way. ie. your product against a similar product.

5.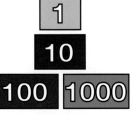

Quantity

Could this product be MASS produced - in large or small quantities?
- or is it a one-off?

6.

Market Sector

Compare to competitors -
how does your product compare
• Visually (aesthetics)?
• Functionally?

And finally ...

Ask other people what they think of your product, - then quote them!